Hands-on Science

CD LINKED

36 fun science activities

Motivate

Experience

Explain

Apply

Review and reflect

6515C

HANDS-ON SCIENCE *(Middle)*

Published by Prim-Ed Publishing 2008
Reprinted under licence by Prim-Ed Publishing 2008
Copyright© R.I.C. Publications® 2007
ISBN 978-1-84654-143-8
PR–6515

Additional titles available in this series:
HANDS-ON SCIENCE *(Lower)*
HANDS-ON SCIENCE *(Upper)*

Internet websites

In some cases, websites or specific URLs may be recommended. While these are checked and rechecked at the time of publication, the publisher has no control over any subsequent changes which may be made to webpages. It is *strongly* recommended that the class teacher checks *all* URLs before allowing pupils to access them.

View all pages online   **Website:** www.prim-ed.com

Foreword

Hands-on learning is 'learning by doing'. It requires pupils to become active participants as they investigate, experiment, design, create, role-play, cook and more, gaining an understanding of essential scientific concepts from these experiences.

Hands-on learning motivates pupils and engages them in their learning. Instead of being told 'why' something occurs, they see it for themselves, directly observing science in action.

The fun, pupil-oriented activities in the *Hands-on science* series teach scientific concepts and skills, while promoting pupil participation, enthusiasm and curiosity about science. Easily integrated into any primary science programme, *Hands-on science* provides clear, step-by-step instructions for each activity and comprehensive background information for the teacher. A glossary of scientific terms used is also included.

Hands-on science provides pupils with the opportunity to enhance their knowledge of the world around them and to engage in collaborative, fun learning that makes science interesting and exciting!

This book is also provided in digital format on the accompanying CD.

Titles in this series are: *Hands-on Science Lower*
Hands-on Science Middle
Hands-on Science Upper

Contents

Teacher information

Each book in the *Hands-on science* series is divided into four science topics:

- Earth and beyond
- Energy and change
- Life and living
- Natural and processed materials

Each section contains nine activities. Each activity is accompanied by a teachers page which includes information to assist the teacher with the activity.

One or more **objectives** are given for each activity page, providing the teacher with the focus of the activity and the behaviours pupils should demonstrate by completing the activity.

The required **materials** are listed clearly so the teacher is aware of what is needed to complete the activity.

Ideas listed under the **motivate** heading include suggested short activities or discussion topics designed to capture the pupils' attention and spark an interest in the lesson. By listening to pupil responses and through observation, teachers will become aware of their pupils' background knowledge.

A 'Before and after' framework, located on page xvii, can also be used to elicit pupils' prior knowledge on a topic.

The **experience** section provides easy to follow instructions for the hands-on activity. The accompanying worksheet may list the step-by-step instructions or be where pupils record their observations and ideas after completing the task.

The **explain** section introduces the conceptual tools pupils need to interpret evidence and construct explanations, allowing them to record, discuss or present their understanding of the scientific concept experienced. It also provides the teacher with important background information about the topic (highlighted in the box).

Another opportunity for pupils to display their understanding of the concept is offered in the **apply** section. It allows pupils to apply their new knowledge and understanding to a different situation.

The **review and reflect** section asks pupils to complete an activity that evaluates their conceptual understanding of the concept. The teacher can use the result as evidence for assessment, demonstrating if understanding of the learning objective has been achieved.

Answers may be included, where appropriate.

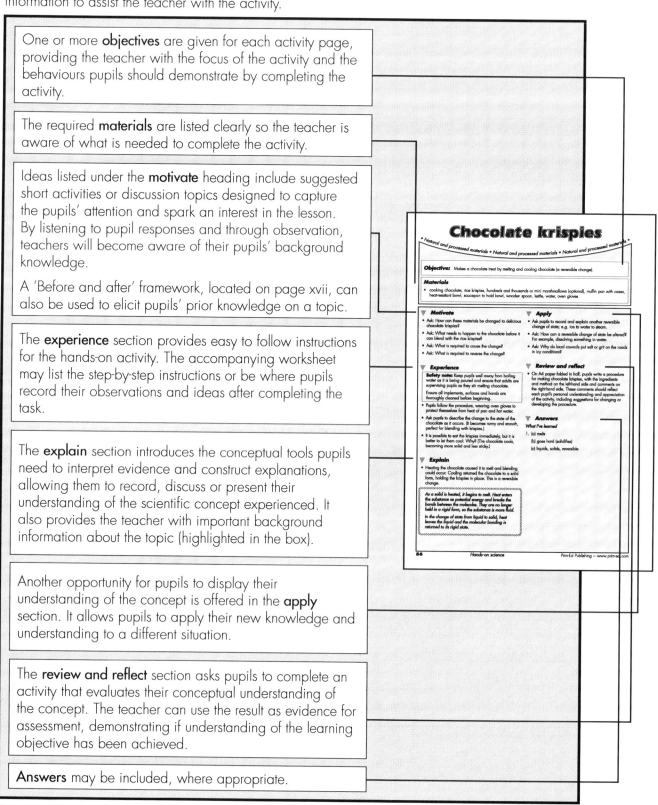

Teacher information

The pupil pages contain a variety of activities. They may be the focus of the lesson, providing step-by-step instructions to complete the hands-on experience, or provide a structure for pupils to record their observations, investigations, results and discoveries.

The **task** is clearly stated at the top of the page, providing a focus for the pupils.

If an activity requires pupils to use material or a tool that is a **possible safety hazard** (such as hot water), the worksheet reminds them to be cautious.

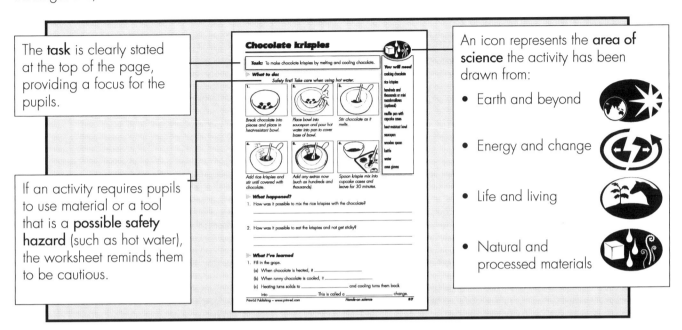

An icon represents the **area of science** the activity has been drawn from:

- Earth and beyond
- Energy and change
- Life and living
- Natural and processed materials

Frameworks

Located at the front of the book are frameworks pupils can use to display their understanding of a scientific concept and experience, and to reinforce concepts learned. The frameworks can be used to plan a new investigation or to reflect upon a completed activity. As pupils write science reports, recounts and investigations, they will be integrating science with literacy. References to relevant frameworks can be found on the accompanying teachers page of a hands-on activity.

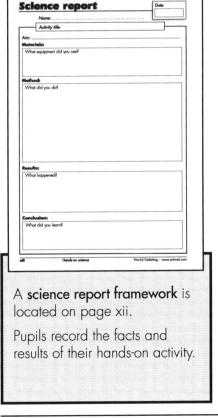

A **science report framework** is located on page xii.

Pupils record the facts and results of their hands-on activity.

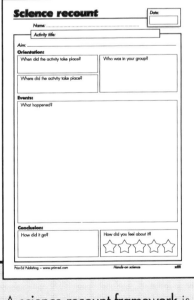

A **science recount framework** is located on page xiii.

Pupils retell the events of their hands-on activity.

A **science investigation framework** is located on page xiv.

Pupils plan a scientific investigation and record their observations.

A **science journal framework** is located on page xv.

Pupils keep a dated record of observations and reflections.

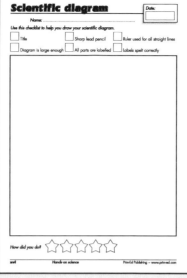

A **scientific diagram framework** is located on page xvi.

After completing a hands-on activity, pupils draw a diagram.

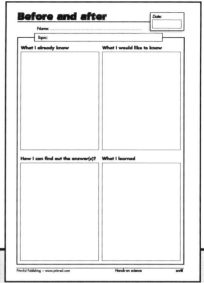

A **before and after chart** is located on page xvii.

Pupils record their prior knowledge of a topic and write questions they hope to answer. Pupils then reflect upon this after completion.

Why 'hands on'?

Hands-on learning is 'learning by doing'. A hands-on approach requires pupils to become active participants in their learning. Pupils investigate and test basic scientific principles by experimenting, creating, designing, cooking and much more, gaining an understanding of the concepts from their experiences.

Many believe that information gained through hands-on learning is remembered and retrieved better, allowing it to be transferred to other situations more easily.

Hands-on learning motivates pupils and engages them in their learning. They develop a curiosity and are interested to know 'why' something occurs. Instead of being told 'why', pupils see it for themselves, directly observing science in action.

Hands-on learning encourages questioning about the events pupils observe and the results they achieve. Pupils improve their scientific skills, such as measuring, observing, predicting and inferring.

Most of the hands-on activities in the book are conducted in groups. Collaborative learning encourages pupils to communicate clearly and express their ideas about science.

Safety

The activities in the *Hands-on science* series are safe for pupils. However, accidents can, and do, happen, and so safety precautions for certain activities are given on the teachers page. Some activities also have a 'Safety note' written on the worksheet to remind pupils. It is imperative that the teacher is aware of possible safety precautions prior to an activity. If careful supervision is required during a lesson, it may be best to organise an additional adult to be in the classroom for that activity.

Science safety tips:

* Try the activity yourself before you present it to the class.

* Ensure that all groups understand the instructions; all pupils are organised and focused on the task.

* Make sure pupils are within view at all times.

* Do not hand out equipment until it is required.

* Remind pupils that they should never taste or smell any materials in a science experiment unless permission is granted by the teacher.

* If an activity is conducted in an outside area, visit the site before hand to ensure it is safe and that examples of what is to be observed are present.

Teacher information

Assessment

An assessment objective for each activity is located on the teachers page. It can be transferred to the assessment proforma on page x.

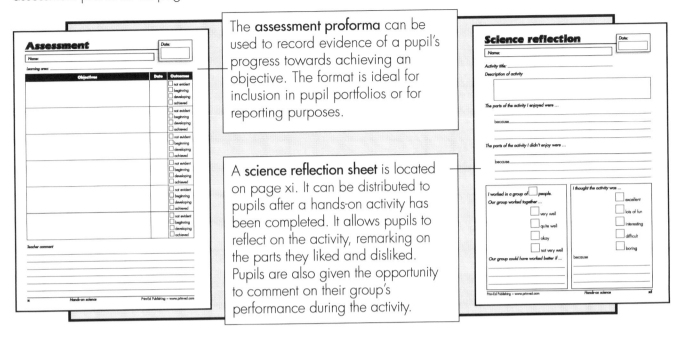

The **assessment proforma** can be used to record evidence of a pupil's progress towards achieving an objective. The format is ideal for inclusion in pupil portfolios or for reporting purposes.

A **science reflection sheet** is located on page xi. It can be distributed to pupils after a hands-on activity has been completed. It allows pupils to reflect on the activity, remarking on the parts they liked and disliked. Pupils are also given the opportunity to comment on their group's performance during the activity.

Curriculum links

	Objectives	Pages
Wales – Science – KS2	• know how the position of the sun appears to change during the day and how shadows change as this happens	2–7
	• describe and group rocks on the basis of appearance and texture and soils on the basis of particle size and permeability	8–17
	• know that mixing materials can cause them to change	18–19
	• know that heating or cooling materials can cause them to change	22–23 & 56–57
	• know sounds are made when objects vibrate and that vibrations from sound sources can travel through a variety of materials to the ear	24–25
	• know some materials are better electrical conductors/insulators than others	26–27
	• know about friction as a force which slows moving objects	28–29
	• know about the forces of attraction between magnets and some materials	30–31
	• know that forces act in particular directions	32–33
	• investigate the effect on the growth of plants of changing their conditions	38–41
	• know about the main stages in the life cycle of flowering plants	42–43
	• find out about the variety of plants and animals found in different habitats	44–45
	• know how plants and animals are suited to their environment	44–45
	• know about the importance of dental care	46–47
	• know that the heart acts as a pump and how blood circulates in the body through arteries and veins	48–49
	• know humans have skeletons to support and protect their bodies and help them move	52–53
	• know about the effect of exercise and rest on pulse rate	54–55
	• know that dissolving, melting, freezing and evaporating are changes that can be reversed	56–59 & 62–63
	• know that irreversible changes result in a new material being formed	64–65
	• know that some materials are better thermal insulators than others	66–67
	• know that solid particles of different sizes can be separated by sieving	72–73

Curriculum links

Objectives	Pages
• recognise that the sun gives us heat and light without which people and animals could not survive	2–7
• investigate different types of rock and soil in the locality	8–17
• investigate how materials may be changed by mixing	10–11
• explore the effects of heating and cooling on a range of liquids, solids and gases	18–19
• learn that light is a form of energy	20–21
• recognise that light comes from different natural and artificial sources	20–21
• understand that the sun is the Earth's most important heat source	22–23
• learn that sound is a form of energy	24–25
• explore the fact that sound travels through materials	24–25
• examine and group materials as conductors and insulators	26–27
• explore the effect of friction on movement through experimenting with toys and objects on various surfaces	28–29
• learn that magnets can push or pull magnetic materials	30–31
• examine and classify objects and materials as magnetic and non-magnetic	30–31
• investigate the relationships between light and materials	34–35
• become aware of the importance of the Earth's renewable and non-renewable resources	36–37
• investigate the factors that affect plant growth	38–43
• develop an increasing awareness of plants	38–43
• understand that plants use light energy from the sun	38–43
• observe, identify and investigate the animals and plants that live in local environments	44–45
• become aware of the names and structure of the body's circulatory system	48–49
• become aware of and investigate breathing	50–51
• explore and investigate the skeleton	52–53
• explore the effects of heating and cooling on a range of liquids, solids and gases, e.g. using a microwave	56–59 & 64–65
• explore some simple ways in which materials may be separated	72–73

Republic of Ireland – Science – 3rd-4th Class

Objectives	Pages
• make connections between the shape, position and size of shadows and the Sun at different times of the day	4–7
• investigate melting, freezing and boiling and relate findings to everyday experiences, including weather	10–11 & 56–57
• use knowledge of light, sound and senses to demonstrate and evaluate simple methods of communication	20–21 & 24–25
• explore the forces exerted by magnets	30–31
• explore links between how far things move and the force applied	32–33
• find out what plants need in order to grow and develop, observe and record findings and grow healthy plants in school	38–41
• understand ways to keep teeth healthy	46–47
• know the position and function of the major organs of the body	48–51
• explore the properties of different materials and choose appropriate materials to solve a practical challenge	66–69
• take part in activities which demonstrate simple chemical reactions safely using everyday 'kitchen chemicals'	10–11, 22–23, 56–57 & 64–65
• investigate the properties of light and show how these can be used in a creative way	20–21
• use simple components in a series circuit and explain in simple terms why the circuit works	26–27
• explain how friction affects movement	28–29
• discuss why it is important to the future of the world that alternatives to fossil fuels are developed	36–37
• present a visual representation explaining plant reproduction	42–43
• compare the thermal insulating properties of materials and choose the most appropriate material for a particular purpose	66–67
• evaluate the effectiveness of a material for its purpose	66–69
• use knowledge of separation techniques to solve problems or challenges in a scientific way	72–73

Scotland – Science — First (P4/P5) / Second (P4/P5)

Curriculum links

Assessment

Name:

Learning area: _____

Objectives	Date	Outcomes
		☐ not evident ☐ beginning ☐ developing ☐ achieved
		☐ not evident ☐ beginning ☐ developing ☐ achieved
		☐ not evident ☐ beginning ☐ developing ☐ achieved
		☐ not evident ☐ beginning ☐ developing ☐ achieved
		☐ not evident ☐ beginning ☐ developing ☐ achieved
		☐ not evident ☐ beginning ☐ developing ☐ achieved

Teacher comment

_____

_____

_____

_____

_____

Science reflection

Date:

Name:

Activity title: _____

Description of activity

The parts of the activity I enjoyed were …

_____

because _____

_____

_____ .

The parts of the activity I didn't enjoy were …

_____

because _____

_____

_____ .

I worked in a group of ☐ people.

Our group worked together …

☐ very well

☐ quite well

☐ okay

☐ not very well

Our group could have worked better if …

_____

_____ .

I thought the activity was …

☐ excellent

☐ lots of fun

☐ interesting

☐ difficult

☐ boring

because _____

_____

_____ .

Science report

Date:

Name: ....

Activity title:

Aim: _____

Materials:

What equipment did you use?

Method:

What did you do?

Results:

What happened?

Conclusion:

What did you learn?

Science recount

Name: ....

Activity title:

Aim: _____

Orientation:

When did the activity take place?	Who was in your group?

Where did the activity take place?

Events:

What happened?

Conclusion:

How did it go?	How did you feel about it?
	☆ ☆ ☆ ☆ ☆

Science investigation

Date:

Name: ....

Activity title:

Clarification:

What is being investigated?

Planning:

What equipment will you use?

Activities:

How was the investigation carried out?

Observations:

What did you find out?

Recommendations:

What would you do differently next time?

Science journal

Name: ....

Activity title:

Observations and ideas	Data and diagrams

Date:

Date:

Date:

Date:

Date:

Scientific diagram

Name: ....

Use this checklist to help you draw your scientific diagram.

- ☐ Title
- ☐ Sharp lead pencil
- ☐ Ruler used for all straight lines
- ☐ Diagram is large enough
- ☐ All parts are labelled
- ☐ Labels spelt correctly

How did you do? ☆☆☆☆☆

Before and after

Name: ....

Topic:

What I already know

What I would like to know

How I can find out the answer(s)?

What I learned

Glossary

absorbency: the amount of liquid a substance can take in before it is saturated.

absorption: the process in which one substance permeates another.

acid: a chemical compound containing hydrogen which can neutralise alkalis.

acidity: the amount of acid present in a substance.

alkali: a chemical compound containing hydroxide which can neutralise acids.

axis: a straight line running through an object; the Earth's axis is an imaginary line that runs through the North and South Poles.

battery: a source that stores electrical energy.

blend: to mix, so that neither component can be separated.

BPM (beats per minute): how many times the heart beats in a minute.

bulb: glass container with incandescent filament which glows when electrical current passes through it.

buzzer: signalling device which produces sound by the vibration of moving parts when a magnetic field is created by electrical current.

carbon: a naturally occurring element.

carbonisation: the formation of carbon through burning a substance.

change (of state): to change a substance from a solid to a liquid, to a gas and back again.

charring: burning to form carbon.

chemical change: irreversible change caused by alteration to the chemical structure of a material.

clay: a sticky soil that hardens when dried.

control: a variable that is held constant in an experiment.

cooling: effect of reducing temperature.

crystals: solid particles remaining after evaporation of water from a solution.

denature: the breaking down of internal bonds within proteins.

dissolve: to mix a soluble solute in a solvent.

electrical circuit: a closed route carrying an electric current.

electrical conductivity: the property of allowing electricity to pass through an object.

electrical conductor: a material that allows the flow of electricity through it.

electrical current: the flow of electrical charges.

enamel: the outer part of the crowns of teeth.

evaporation: the changing of water into a gaseous state by way of heat.

fair test: a science experiment in which all the variables need to stay the same, except for the one being tested.

friction: the force that acts against a moving object.

gas: a state of matter in which molecules are free to fill the whole space of a given container.

germinate: to sprout and send out shoots.

gnomon: the raised section on a sundial that casts a shadow.

granite: a hard, grainy igneous rock formed from cooled magma.

habitat: where an organism lives.

heartbeat: the sound the heart makes as it pumps blood around the body.

heating: the effect of increasing temperature.

Glossary

homogeneous: .... all parts of the mix are exactly the same.

igneous rock: .... rock formed from cooled lava or magma.

insulator: .... a material that prevents the flow of electricity through it.

irreversible: .... cannot be returned to its former state.

lava: .... molten rock that has erupted from a volcano.

liquid: .... state of matter in which molecules are free to move among themselves, but not into air.

loam: .... a rich, fertile soil containing sand, clay and humus.

magma: .... molten rock found beneath the Earth's surface.

melt: .... when a substance is changing from a solid to a liquid state.

mineral: .... a naturally occurring substance formed through a geological process, usually having a crystalline form.

molecular bonding: .... the structure of the bonds holding the molecules of a substance together.

molecule: .... a very small particle of a substance.

neutral: .... neither acid nor alkaline.

non-renewable energy sources: . energy sources that are going to run out one day and cannot be recreated; e.g. fossil fuels—petroleum, coal and gas.

obelisk: .... a stone tower with a pyramid-shaped top, used as a shadow clock in ancient times.

obsidian: .... a hard, glassy igneous rock.

organism: .... a living thing, animal or plant.

particles: .... pieces of a material/compound.

pH: .... degree of acidity.

physical change: .... reversible change to a substance from one state to another, which can then revert to its original form.

pulse: .... the rhythm of the heart beating.

pumice: .... a lightweight igneous rock.

renewable energy sources: .... energy sources that are created naturally and can replace themselves (which means they are sustainable); solar, wind, water, tidal, wave, geothermal, biomass etc.

sand: .... a dry, mainly siliceous soil.

saturation: .... when no more solute can be dissolved in a solvent.

separation: .... when two or more materials are physically removed from one another.

sieving: .... a process for separating material particles of different size.

solid: .... state of matter in which molecules are rigidly held together.

solubility: .... the extent to which a solute can dissolve in a solvent.

solute: .... the material being dissolved in a solvent.

solution: .... the resultant compound of dissolving a solute in a solvent.

solvent: .... the material in which a solute is dissolved to form a solution.

soundwaves: .... vibrations of particles in a solid, liquid or gas causing sounds to be transferred.

sundial: .... a timekeeping device made from a dial plate and a raised section that casts a shadow.

weathering: .... a physical or chemical process that breaks down or wears away rock.

Day and night

Objective: Uses a model to demonstrate how day and night occur.

Materials

- For each group of pupils – a large polystyrene ball, a torch, a black marker, 2 toothpicks
- A globe of the Earth (see 'Motivate')

▼ Motivate

- Ask what causes the Earth to light up during the day. Is it daytime all over the world at the same time? Why not?

- Use a globe of the world to show the pupils how the earth spins on its axis and the fact that it takes 24 hours to complete one rotation.

▼ Experience

- Organise the pupils into groups and distribute the materials.

- Read the worksheet with the class. Explain that the pupils have to decide how to use the materials to demonstrate day and night; however, some hints about shining the torch while the Earth spins could be provided! The classroom lights should be dimmed/ curtains closed to help pupils see the effect of the torch beams more clearly.

- The groups complete the 'What happened?' questions on their worksheet and then share their results with the class.

- The pupils complete 'What I've learned' individually. Once again, answers can be shared with the class.

▼ Explain

- Depending on the ability of the class, teachers could explain that as the Earth spins, it also revolves around the sun. This could be demonstrated by one pupil shining a torch while another pupil holds the globe of the Earth and, while spinning the globe, circles the other pupil.

Although it appears that the sun moves across the sky, it is actually an illusion. It is the Earth spinning on its axis (anticlockwise) that gives us day and night. The Earth takes 24 hours to completely rotate on its axis—this equals one day. When the sun shines on a part of the Earth, it is daytime. The side of the Earth that is facing away from the sun is in darkness and so it is night-time for that side.

▼ Apply

- Have groups of pupils plan and present role-plays which demonstrate the relationship between the sun and the Earth.

▼ Review and reflect

- Pupils can plan and write a picture book for younger pupils to explain how day and night occur.

Day and night

Task: To use a model to demonstrate how day and night occur.

You will need

a large polystyrene ball

torch

black marker

2 toothpicks

What to do:

1. Push the toothpicks into the polystyrene ball, as shown.

2. Use the marker to draw a small stick figure person on the ball.

3. Using the torch to represent the sun and the polystyrene ball to represent the Earth, find a way to demonstrate how day and night occur for the person you drew on the Earth. (Hint: Have one member of your group hold the polystyrene ball by the toothpicks; have another member of your group hold the torch.)

What happened?

1. Describe what your group did to demonstrate how day and night occur.

_____

_____

_____

2. Do you think this experiment was a good way to demonstrate how day and night occur? How could it be improved?

_____

_____

_____

What I've learned

1. Write a sentence to explain why it takes 24 hours for one whole day and night to happen on Earth.

_____

_____

2. If you could stand on the sun (ouch!), would you ever see the Earth in darkness?

Yes ◯   No ◯

Explain your answer. _____

_____

_____

The long and short of shadows

Objectives:
- Demonstrates how shadows change in length throughout the day.
- Creates a piece of artwork using silhouettes.

Materials

- For each pair of pupils – a small doll or action figure, two sheets of white card, a torch, pencil, glue, scissors, black paper, large sheet of coloured card or paper

▼ Motivate

- On a sunny day, take the pupils outside in the morning, at midday and in the afternoon. Ask them to observe how the length of their shadows change.

▼ Experience

- Organise the pupils into pairs and distribute the materials. Be sure the pupils understand that the task is a simulation of the sun shining on a person.

- Have the pupils write their predictions.

- Explain that as the Earth spins on its axis, the sun will appear to change its position in the sky. At midday, the sun will be directly overhead. Early in the morning and late in the afternoon, it will appear low in the sky. These different positions affect the length of the shadows you see throughout the day.

- Dim the lights or draw the curtains so the pupils can clearly see the shadows they are creating. One person in each pair should hold the torch and the other should draw the shadows. They may need to vary the distance the torch is held from the doll to create darker, more defined shadows.

- Before the pupils begin their artwork, they could discuss how they created their shadows.

- The white card templates could be used to make two silhouettes or more, depending on the size of the coloured card/paper provided and what sort of pattern the pupils wish to create.

- When the artwork is completed, the pupils can write how they created their long and short shadows and copy this onto the back of their artwork. They can then complete the final sentences on the worksheet.

▼ Explain

- The concept could be further consolidated by explaining to the pupils that their shadows changed throughout the day because the Earth spins – therefore changing their position in relation to the sun.

> Shadows are longest in the early morning and late afternoon and shortest at midday. The length of a shadow changes as the sun appears at different angles in the sky. The position of the sun changes as the Earth rotates on its axis.
>
> The sun appears to rise in the east and set in the west because the Earth spins on its axis from west to east (anticlockwise).

▼ Apply

- Have the pupils draw their own shadows, using chalk, – in the morning, at midday and in the afternoon (while standing on the same spot) – and measure the shadow length from where the pupil stood. Pupils could also try to predict where their shadows will move to throughout the day.

▼ Review and reflect

- Pupils complete the science report on page xii, to explain what happened during their shadow experiment.

The long and short of shadows

Task: To demonstrate how shadows change in length throughout the day.

You will need

a partner

a small doll or action figure

two sheets of white card

torch

glue

pencil

scissors

black paper

a large sheet of coloured card or paper

Try this demonstration to discover how the length of a person's shadow changes with the movement and position of the sun—and create a work of art at the same time!

▶ What will happen?

Tick which of these you think will create the longest shadow:

☐ Shining the torch directly down on the action figure (the same as the sun at noon)

☐ Shining the torch on the side of the action figure (the same as the sun in the early morning or late afternoon)

▶ What to do:

1. Stand your action figure on a sheet of white card. One person should shine the torch beam directly down on the action figure, staying as still as possible. Draw the outline of the shadow that is created.

2. Now stand your action figure on the second sheet of white card. Shine the torch beam onto the side of the action figure. Draw the outline of this shadow.

3. Cut out, along the outlines, the shadows you have created. Use them as templates to trace them onto a sheet of black paper. Cut out these black paper shapes. Glue the shadows onto a coloured sheet of paper or card to create a pattern.

▶ What happened?

1. Write how you created the shorter shadow and how you created the longer shadow.

_____

_____

2. Copy this sentence onto the back of your artwork.

▶ What I've learned

1. If the sun appears low in the sky, an object's shadow will be _____.

2. If the sun appears high overhead, an object's shadow will be _____.

Dialling the sun

Objective: Creates and monitors a simple sundial.

Materials

- For each group of pupils – a broomstick, a black marker, 6 large stones or rocks (each of which is able to have a number written on it). The broomsticks will need to stand vertically in the ground; if the sundials are to be created on a hard surface, the broomsticks could be planted in buckets filled with sand.

- Instead of the pupils drawing their results, photographs could be taken of each sundial and then glued into the space provided on the worksheet.

- Teachers will need to choose an area in the school that receives sun throughout the day and will not be disturbed by other pupils.

- A sunny day is needed for this activity. At least one member of each group will need to be able to check the sundial between 10 am and 3 pm on the hour, every hour.

▼ Motivate

- Look at photographs and pictures of sundials.
- Discuss how sundials, shadow sticks and obelisks were often used by ancient cultures to tell the time.

▼ Experience

- Organise the pupils into groups and distribute the materials. The groups can then set up their sundials and monitor them throughout the day. The worksheet can then be completed and the answers shared with the class.

- The next day, if time permits, pupils could again check the sundials to see if they correspond with the previous results.

▼ Explain

- Discuss how, as the Earth rotates on its axis, the sun appears to move across the sky. The shadows cast by the sun therefore move during the day—in a clockwise direction in the northern hemisphere and an anticlockwise direction in the southern hemisphere. Because of the Earth's rotation and revolution around the sun, sundials only remain accurate in one position for about two weeks.

In this activity, strictly speaking, the pupils are monitoring a 'shadow stick', not a sundial. Because the Earth is curved, the ground at the base of a shadow stick will not be at the same angle to the sun's rays as it is at the equator. Therefore, the shadow caused by a shadow stick will not move at a uniform rate.

A commercial sundial is usually made of a dial plate marked out with hour lines and a raised section called a 'gnomon' that casts a shadow. The inclined edge of the gnomon is called the 'style' and the shadow of this edge is used to tell the time. A sundial must be made specifically for the spot where it will be used and pointed in the right direction.

▼ Apply

- Research and make variations of this sundial using different materials, or observe a commercial sundial to see how it works.

▼ Review and reflect

- Design and make a portable sundial (e.g. a 'wristwatch' sundial or 'necklace' sundial) based on the concepts covered in this activity.

Dialling the sun

| **Task:** To create and monitor a sundial. |

You will need

broomstick

black marker

6 large stones or rocks

What to do:

1. Write one of these numbers on each rock to represent different hours of the day: '10', '11', '12', '1', '2' and '3'.

2. With your group, position the broomstick so it is standing vertically in a place that receives sunlight throughout the day.

3. Between 10 am and 3 pm, check the shadow that is created by the broomstick on the hour, every hour. Use one of your 'time stones' to mark where the end of each shadow reaches.

4. Show your results in the space below by drawing a diagram of the six rocks.

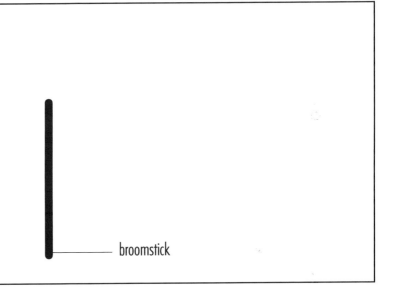

broomstick

What happened?

1. Explain what happened to the shadow as the day progressed.

_____

_____

2. What are the problems with a sundial compared to an ordinary clock?

_____

_____

_____

3. How do you think you could improve your sundial?

_____

_____

Weathered rocks

Objectives:
- Conducts experiments to demonstrate physical and chemical weathering.
- Understands some differences between physical and chemical weathering.

Materials

- For each group of pupils – an eye-dropper; a few tablespoons of vinegar; a piece of chalk; a plastic jar with a lid; a handful of small, jagged stones; a small ball of clay; a ziplock bag; a small piece of steel wool and a saucer with water. Teachers may also like to provide gloves for the pupils when handling the steel wool. A freezer is also required.

▼ Motivate

- Pose the question, 'Do rocks last forever?' Ask pupils to explain their answers.
- Show some photographs of well-known rock formations that have weathered over hundreds of years.

▼ Experience

- Read the information at the top of the page with the pupils and discuss any examples they may have seen of weathered rocks.
- Organise the pupils into groups and distribute the materials. Experiment 4 will need to be started by the pupils three days before the worksheet is completed; Experiments 2 and 3 the day before. Alternatively, teachers could prepare these experiments for the pupils in advance, taking care to explain the procedure involved before the pupils make their observations.
- Pupils complete the worksheet. They will need to refer to the information at the top of the page, as well as the results of their experiments, to help them tick the correct sentences. All results/answers can then be discussed by the class.

▼ Explain

- The process of erosion could also be discussed as a continuation of the weathering process, as it carries rock fragments from one place to another using agents such as water, wind and ice. Sometimes human activity speeds up the natural erosion process, sometimes to the detriment of the environment.

Weathering is a slow process that wears away rock. It causes rock to crack, break down, dissolve, crumble or fragment. Physical weathering (also called 'mechanical' weathering) and chemical weathering often occur together in nature. We tend to think of weathering as a negative force, as it can ruin structures (such as buildings), but it is part of an important cycle. Weathered rock eventually creates soil and releases minerals and ores to nourish living things.

▼ Apply

- Try experiments that demonstrate erosion, another process which breaks down rock; for example, blowing on sandcastles through a straw, dripping water onto a tray of soil, dissolving sweets in water.

▼ Review and reflect

- Pupils complete the science recount on page xiii for all four experiments.

▼ Answers

Experiments

1 – The acid in the vinegar should react with the calcium carbonate in the chalk, producing bubbling or fizzing. This demonstrates chemical weathering.

2 – Fragments of rock should have broken off or the stones will have more rounded edges. There should also be some sediment in the water. This demonstrates physical weathering.

3 – The clay should become cracked and broken as the water expands and turns into ice. This demonstrates physical weathering.

4 – Rust should have formed on some parts of the steel wool, just as rocks containing iron react with moisture start to rust and eventually crumble. This demonstrates chemical weathering.

What I've learned

2 what happens to stones carried along by a river.

4 that steel wool contains iron.

3 what happens if water freezes in the cracks of rocks.

1 that vinegar is a type of acid.

Weathered rocks

Task: To demonstrate physical and chemical weathering.

It may seem like rocks last forever—but they don't! A force called weathering constantly breaks rocks down. Weathering can be either a physical or chemical process. Physical weathering takes place when heat, ice, water or wind breaks rocks into smaller pieces. Chemical weathering occurs when a chemical reaction produces a substance that weakens rock. As an example, a chemical reaction might produce an acid (when water mixes with some gases) or rust (when iron mixes with oxygen and water).

You will need

eye-dropper

vinegar

a piece of chalk

plastic jar with lid

handful of small, jagged stones

small ball of clay

ziplock bag

small piece of steel wool

saucer

water

▶ What to do:

Find out for yourself how weathering affects rock. Try each of the experiments below, then explain what happened and what type of weathering it shows.

Procedure	What happened?	Type of weathering
Experiment 1 • Drip a few drops of vinegar on a piece of chalk.		
Experiment 2 • Place stones in a plastic jar. • Half-fill the jar with water and leave it overnight. • Shake the jar 500 times.		
Experiment 3 • Wet a ball of clay. • Place it in a ziplock bag and freeze it overnight.		
Experiment 4 • Wet a piece of steel wool. • Place it on a saucer and leave it for three days.		

▶ What I've learned

Write a number in the box to show which experiment demonstrated:

☐ what happens to stones carried along by a river.

☐ that steel wool contains iron.

☐ what happens if water freezes in the cracks of rocks.

☐ that vinegar is a type of acid.

Edible rocks

Objectives:
- Understands how volcanic lava can change the Earth's surface.
- Observes and identifies simulated igneous rocks.

Materials

- 2 cups of sugar and 1 cup of water for each type of rock; 1 teaspoon of bicarbonate of soda; 1 tablespoon of milk; 3 greased baking trays; saucepan; hotplate; spoon; freezer

▼ Motivate

- Show pupils photographs of volcanoes and, if possible, some samples of real obsidian, granite and pumice.

- Explain to pupils you are going to make some edible rocks.

▼ Experience

- Read the information at the top of the page with the pupils, then perform the cooking demonstration. Be sure to compare the hot sugar mixture to magma/lava. Make sure pupils understand that granite is formed underground from magma, not lava.

- Teachers will need to 'cook' the igneous rocks on a hotplate in front of the pupils. Alternatively, the process could be filmed or photographed and replayed or shown to the pupils.

- For each type of 'rock', place 2 cups of white sugar and 1 cup of water in a saucepan. Stir over a low heat until the sugar is dissolved. Increase the heat and boil for approximately 15 minutes or until the sugar is golden brown. Be careful not to burn the mixture—it will need to be watched carefully as it foams when boiling and this can make the colour difficult to determine. When the mixture is ready, follow the directions below:

  – To make obsidian, pour the hot mixture onto a cold, greased baking tray (sit the tray in a freezer for at least 10 minutes before it is needed) and leave to cool. A glossy sheet of toffee should result.

  – To make pumice, stir 1 teaspoon of bicarbonate of soda into the hot mixture, then pour it onto a cold greased baking tray (sit the tray in a freezer for at least 10 minutes before it is needed) and leave to cool. This should create tiny bubbles of gas, creating a honeycomb-like result.

  – To make granite, add 1 tablespoon of milk to the hot mixture, then pour it onto a room-temperature greased baking tray and let it cool. The caramel-like result should have a grainy texture.

- Organise the pupils into groups and distribute a sample of each type of 'rock'. Pupils can then recall the method used to make each rock and compare it to the information provided on the worksheet. Note-form should be used. They could also draw each of their rock samples.

- Once the pupils have answered Question 2, the answers can be discussed as a class. As part of the discussion, compare the 'rocks' formed from lava (obsidian and pumice) with the 'rock' formed from magma (granite). If all surfaces, utensils and hands were washed thoroughly during the cooking process, the rocks can be eaten.

Safety note: Keep pupils well away from the hot toffee mixture until it has cooled.

▼ Explain

- Discuss how volcanoes can change the surface of the Earth.

> Volcanoes erupt when hot gases inside the Earth build up, pushing magma towards the surface. A volcanic eruption can trigger tsunamis, floods, rock flows, mudflows and earthquakes.
>
> When magma or lava cools, it forms crystals. Lava cools quicker than magma, so its crystals are much smaller and the rock may have a glassy texture. Volcanic rocks formed from lava (also called 'extrusive' igneous rocks) include pumice, obsidian, basalt and rhyolite. Rocks that form from magma (also called 'intrusive' igneous rocks or plutonic rocks) include granite, gabbro and diroite. The composition and characteristics of these rocks depend on the types of minerals present in the ground and, in the case of extrusive igneous rocks, the type of eruption that has occurred; for example, pumice is often the result of an explosive eruption.

▼ Apply

- Make a model volcano by pouring bicarbonate of soda, vinegar and red food colouring into a cardboard cone. Full instructions for this popular experiment can be found by typing 'make a volcano' into an Internet search engine.

▼ Review and reflect

- Pupils research and write an explanation as to how making one type of edible rock is similar to the process that creates its real volcanic rock counterpart.

Edible rocks

Task: To observe and identify simulated igneous rocks.

A volcano is a way by which melted rock (magma) and gas can erupt through the Earth's surface. Once magma has erupted it is called 'lava'. Cooled lava forms a type of rock called 'igneous rock'. Igneous rock can also form underground from magma that doesn't erupt. Over time, igneous rock and other materials ejected from volcanoes can build up on the Earth's surface, creating new land or causing volcanoes to grow in height. There are many types of igneous rocks. Some of these are:

Obsidian: Formed from lava that has cooled very quickly, so it has a smooth appearance. Is often called 'volcanic glass'.

Pumice: Lightweight, frothy-looking rock. Its unique appearance is caused by bubbles of gas trapped in lava as it cooled.

Granite: Formed from magma that cooled very slowly beneath the Earth's surface. It has a grainy texture.

▶ What to do:

1. Watch your teacher cook some edible igneous rocks! Use the clues above and your observations of the cooled 'rock' to help you identify each one.

Method	Appearance when cool	Most similar to …
		☐ obsidian ☐ pumice ☐ granite
		☐ obsidian ☐ pumice ☐ granite
		☐ obsidian ☐ pumice ☐ granite

2. Name two types of igneous rock that can form from volcanic lava.

_____   _____

Studying soils

Objective: Examines and describes three different soils taken from around the school grounds.

Materials

- Prior to the lesson, take a small shovel and a number of jars with screw-top lids and visit areas of the school where there is soil/sand etc. Collect each sample in the jars, taking care not to completely fill them, and label with a number and description of location from where the soil was found. Try to find as many different soils as possible. The number of jars required will depend on the number of groups for the activity.

- Other materials required include: Hands lenses or magnifying glasses, teaspoons, glue

Safety note: Be sure to choose soils that are not contaminated with dog faeces or similar hazards. The pupils can wear disposable gloves for this activity as a precaution.

▼ Motivate

- Ask the pupils what soil is: Are all soils the same? Discuss where we find soil; e.g. at the beach, in the garden. What fun things do children make with soil? (mud pies etc.) What about adults?

▼ Experience

- Organise the pupils into the same number of groups as you have jars of soil.

- Place all of the jars of soil in a tray at the front of the classroom.

- Read the worksheet with the class. The pupils will need to write keywords or phrases to help describe each characteristic.

  – 'Sound' refers to the sound made when the jar is shaken. The answer to this may simply be 'none'.

  – 'Texture' refers to how it feels; soft, grainy, coarse etc.

- Pupils open the jars, remove a small sample of soil using the teaspoon and glue some to their page.

- When a column has been completed, pupils swap their soil with another group. Tell pupils to look for a soil that appears to be different from the one they have just studied.

- When pupils have studied three soils, a class discussion about soil can follow.

  – Groups who have studied the same soil can discuss and compare their descriptions of that soil. Why might there be differences with their descriptions?

▼ Explain

- Explain to the pupils that soil is very important to us because most of our food comes from soil—even the animals we eat live by eating plants grown in soil.

Soils consist of worn-down rock that is mixed with water, air, humus (dead organic matter) and living organisms, like worms. There are many different types of rocks; consequently, there are many different types of soils. The three main soil types are sand, clay and loam.

▼ Apply

- Pupils repeat the activity using a soil sample taken from outside the school (from home, on a school excursion etc.)

Soil separation activity

- Gather soil which contains different-sized particles, pebbles, plant materials and, if possible, living and dead organic matter. Half fill a jar with the sample and add water, taking care to ensure that there is enough space left so the jar can be shaken. Check the lid is screwed on tightly and shake the jar. Leave the jar overnight in a place where it will not be disturbed. Pupils study the jar the next day. On an A4 sheet of paper, pupils draw an outline of the jar, clearly labelling and describing what they see. Pupils could use the scientific diagram framework on page xvi to draw their diagram. Pupils add colour to their diagram.

When soil is shaken in water, and given time to settle, it separates into different sized particles. The heaviest on the bottom and lightest at the top.

▼ Review and reflect

- Create a landscape picture by gluing different soil samples to different parts of the picture. Pupils can explain why they used a particular soil for each part of the picture, referring to its characteristics.

Studying soils

Task: To examine a variety of soil samples taken from different areas around the school.

What to do:

With your group, study each soil sample and complete this table.

	Soil 1	Soil 2	Soil 3
Location found			
Colour			
Smell			
Sound			
Moisture (none, some, lots)			
Texture (rub between your palms)			
Particle size (look through lens— small, medium, large)			
Other observations (pebbles, insects found etc.)			
Soil sample (glue soil here—don't make a mess)			

Surveying soil

Objective: Investigates absorbability of different soils.

Materials

- Three different types of soils—such as sand, clay and potting mix; 3 large jars (to hold soil); labels for jars containing soil.

- For each group: 3 polystyrene cups; pencil; wide-mouthed jar; sheet of paper towel; measuring jug (in mL and with cup measurements); black marker.
  Note: If there are six groups, there will need to be two samples of each type of soil so each group can conduct the test. (Nine groups—three samples of each etc.)

Safety note: Be sure to choose soils that are not contaminated with dog faeces or similar hazards. The pupils can wear disposable gloves for this activity as a precaution.

▼ Motivate

- Ask the pupils if, during a storm, there is sometimes flooding around their house/the school? Why might this be? What do they think would happen if the rainwater didn't run off but stayed in the soil under the houses?

- Show the pupils the three soils they will use for the experiment. Ask them to describe the visual differences between them.

▼ Experience

- Organise the pupils into groups and distribute the materials.

- Read the activity with the class and explain the purpose of the test being performed on each soil.

- It may be useful if the teacher first demonstrates the test and pupils observe.

- Once completed, the pupils write their 'lab report', recommending the soil which absorbs the least amount of water (most amount of water in the jar) and the area which is best suited for a housing development.

▼ Explain

- Discuss with the pupils the three main types of soil and where they might be found.

Potting soil – its main purpose is to retain water for plants and flowers to grow. This type of soil should retain most of the water in the experiment. It would not be suitable for a housing development—except to be used in gardens.

Clay – absorbs water which makes it swell. When the water evaporates, the clay cracks. As water does not move through clay easily, it will hold water in the experiment. It is not the best type of soil for a housing development.

Sand (sandy soil) – will let the most amount of water run through it. Sandy soil is best for housing developments as rain has little effect on the soil and allows the greatest amount of runoff (so the footing of the house is not affected). It should be recommended for the housing development.

▼ Apply

- Pupils give recommendations for usage of the other two soils tested; for example:

  – to be used in the construction of gardens around the new housing development.

  Pupils give reasons for their recommendations.

▼ Review and reflect

- Pupils complete a scientific investigation of the experiment (page xiv).

Surveying soil

Task: To investigate how different types of soils absorb water.

You are a soil expert who has been hired to choose the best of three areas for a new housing development. You must test the soils in each area to see which one allows the most water to flow through it. Houses need to be built on soils that allow runoff from heavy rains, otherwise the moisture stays in the soil causing problems for builders and homeowners.

What to do:

1. Label the cups A, B and C.

2. Use the pencil to punch a hole in the bottom of each polystyrene cup.

3. Line the bottom of the cups with paper towel.

4. Half-fill the cups with each soil and label correctly.

5. Hold Cup A inside the jar and carefully pour 2 cups of water directly over the soil.

6. When the cup stops dripping, pour the water in the jar into the measuring jug.

7. Record your results in the lab report below.

8. Repeat with Soil B and Soil C.

What happened?

You will need

3 different soils (Soil A, Soil B and Soil C)

pencil

3 polystyrene cups

black marker

a sheet of paper towel

a wide-mouthed jar

measuring jug (in mL and with cup measurements)

SOIL REPORT

Soil expert: .... Date: ....

Results of water absorption tests on Soil A, B and C are as follows:

Soil	A	B	C
Amount of water not absorbed by soil (in mL).			

Sketch of test conducted (labelled)

My recommendations:

The area with soil type ☐ will be best for a housing development because

_____

_____

_____

Signed: ....

Let's rock!

Objective: Classifies rocks according to their observable characteristics.

Materials

- For each group of pupils, prepare sets of four different rocks (each set should contain rocks of different weights, grain textures and hardness). At least one rock should contain calcium carbonate (e.g. limestone). They will also need an eye-dropper, water, paperclip, vinegar and a set of scales.

▼ Motivate

- Show the pupils a set of four different rocks and demonstrate the tests described on the worksheet to show how they are different (see 'Experience' for detailed description of how to perform the tests.) Ask the pupils to name any other differences they observe or know of (e.g. differences between the way rocks are formed).

▼ Experience

- Organise the pupils into groups and distribute the materials.

- Discuss the sample experiments that were performed (see 'Motivate') and explain each test in more detail. For 'Texture', the pupils need to look closely at each rock to decide whether or not they can see its mineral grains. If so, the rock is coarsely-grained. If not, the rock is finely-grained. For permeability, the pupils should use the eye-dropper to drop five drops of water on each rock, then watch closely to see if any of the water is absorbed. For 'Scratched by', the pupils should try scratching the rock with a fingernail, then with the end of a straightened-out paperclip. For 'Streaks on concrete', the pupils will need to go outside the classroom and rub the rock along a concrete footpath or area. For 'Fizzes with vinegar', the pupils need to drop five drops of vinegar on the rock to see if it fizzes (the fizzing indicates the presence of calcium carbonate). For 'Weight', pupils weigh each rock individually on a scale.

- Once the groups have completed their tests, they can complete the 'Rock records' at the bottom of the page for their set of rocks. If teachers know the different rock types that were given to the pupils, the names can be revealed and pupils can write these along with 'Rock 1', 'Rock 2' etc.

▼ Explain

- Rocks have a variety of properties. These include colour, lustre (shininess) and hardness. We can classify rocks by sight, touch and weight.

The Mohs hardness scale is a universal scale used to distinguish the hardness of minerals. The higher the number, the harder the mineral. The scale is as follows:

1. *Talc*
2. *Gypsum*
3. *Calcite*
4. *Fluorite*
5. *Apatite*
6. *Orthoclase*
7. *Quartz*
8. *Topaz*
9. *Corundum (ruby and sapphire)*
10. *Diamond*

▼ Apply

- Have the pupils collect their own rocks from the local area and group them according to differences in texture or other criteria.

▼ Review and reflect

- Pupils create charts showing the results of their experiment, including samples of their rocks.

Let's rock!

Task: To classify rocks according to their observable characteristics.

▶ What to do:

Follow the directions below for each rock. Record your results in the table.

(a) Examine the texture of the rock's grains.

(b) Use water drops to test for water absorption (permeability).

(c) Try to scratch the rock; first with your fingernail and then with a paperclip.

(d) Rub the rock on concrete to see if it creates a mark.

(e) Use vinegar to test for fizziness (carbonate).

(f) Weigh the rock.

You will need

4 rocks

eye-dropper

water

paperclip (straightened out)

vinegar

set of scales

	Rock 1	Rock 2	Rock 3	Rock 4
Texture				
Permeability				
Scratched by:				
• fingernail				
• paperclip				
Streaks on concrete				
Fizzes with vinegar				
Weight				

▶ What I've learned

Rock records!

Most finely-grained _____

Most coarsely-grained _____

Most permeable _____

Softest _____

Hardest _____

Contained carbonate _____

Heaviest _____

Lightest _____

Creating crystals

Objective: Grows salt and bicarbonate of soda crystals.

Materials

- For each group: approx. 5 tablespoons of sea salt; 1 tablespoon of bicarbonate of soda; teaspoons; boiling water; 2 glass jars; 2 pencils; 2 paperclips—each tied to a 10-cm length of string; paper towel; food colouring
- Adult helpers will be required to assist with the boiling water.

▼ Motivate

- Show the pupils examples or photographs of some mineral crystals, such as quartz, diamond and rock salt. Discuss the differences between them.

- To help the pupils grasp the concept of rocks being made up of two or more minerals, show them a chocolate chip biscuit and ask them to imagine it as a rock. Ask them what ingredients make up the biscuit; e.g. flour, sugar, chocolate chips. Explain that these ingredients are like the minerals that make up a rock.

▼ Experience

- Organise the pupils into groups and distribute the materials.

- Read the information at the top of the page and the instructions for the experiment with the pupils. Allocate an adult helper to each group to pour the boiling water. Suggest that group members take turns to stir teaspoons of salt or bicarbonate of soda into the jars. Explain to the pupils that some patience is required—the dry ingredients must dissolve properly for the experiment to work. It will take approximately 1 tablespoon of bicarbonate of soda and 5 tablespoons of salt in total to make a 'saturated solution'—one which has a small amount of salt or soda left at the bottom of the jar that will not dissolve.

Safety note: Keep the pupils away from the boiling water as it is poured and ensure that adults are supervising as pupils stir the salt and bicarbonate of soda into the hot water.

- Once the pupils have placed their paperclips and string, the jars should be put in an area where they will not be disturbed for a week. For this experiment to work it is most important that the jars are not moved. The jars should also be covered lightly with a square of paper towel to prevent dust entering the solutions. The pupils can then check their jars at the time intervals given on the worksheet.

- After 24 hours, some small crystals should be able to be seen forming at the bottom of the jar, on the surface of the water and/or on the string and paper clip. After a week, some of the water should have evaporated and the crystals can (carefully) be taken out of the jars

to display. Salt should form cube-shaped crystals, while bicarbonate of soda crystals will have a feathered appearance.

▼ Explain

- Explain to the pupils that all rocks are made up of two or more minerals. Most minerals occur naturally as crystals and grow in liquids. Rock crystals often form in magma (molten rock). When the magma cools, some atoms bond together and form crystals. The crystals then grow by adding atoms to their surfaces in a repeated pattern.

The process by which crystals form is called 'nucleation'. During nucleation, the atoms that will crystallise are dissolved. These dissolved particles then bond with each other until a crystal nucleus is formed. Other atoms then connect to the surface of the crystal, making it grow. The crystal will continue to grow until a balance is achieved between the atoms in the new crystal and those left in the solution.

Every crystal has an internal pattern of atoms. The shape of a crystal, such as a six-sided snowflake or four-sided salt crystal, reflects its internal pattern.

To grow a crystal, it is necessary to use a saturated solution—one which increases the chances of the solute atoms forming a nucleus. It is also useful to provide a rough surface on which the atoms can 'meet' and therefore achieve nucleation; for example, a piece of string.

▼ Apply

- Have the pupils try growing crystals with sugar or epsom salts and/or change some of the other variables of the original experiment; such as the heat of the water, not using string, leaving for a longer period of time etc.

▼ Review and reflect

- Pupils use the worksheet on page xvi to draw labelled scientific diagrams of their experiment one day, and then one week into the experiment.

Creating crystals

You will need

sea salt

bicarbonate of soda

teaspoons

boiling water

2 glass jars

2 pencils

2 paperclips, each tied to a length of string

paper towel

food colouring

Rocks are made up of substances called minerals. Some minerals you might know are gold, salt, diamond and quartz. Most minerals occur naturally as crystals. Crystals may take thousands of years to form, but some can 'grow' quickly.

Try growing salt and bicarbonate of soda crystals.

► What to do:

> **Safety first!** *Take care when using hot water.*

1. Have an adult pour about $^1/_2$ a cup of boiling water into each jar. Add a few drops of food colouring to each jar. Label one jar 'Salt' and the other 'Bicarbonate of soda'.

2. Add the salt and bicarbonate of soda to the appropriate jar, one teaspoonful at time. After each teaspoon has been added, stir until it is completely dissolved. Eventually, you will find that a small amount of salt/bicarbonate of soda will not dissolve and collects at the bottom of the jar. When this happens, you are ready to make crystals!

3. Place the paperclip and string into the jars. Wind the end of the string around a pencil until the paperclip just touches the bottom of the jar when the pencil is placed on top of the jar. Place the jars in a protected area and cover with paper towel.

► What happened?

Check your jars at each of the intervals below. Write what you see.

	Salt	Bicarbonate of soda
1 day		
2 days		
4 days		
1 week		

► What I've learned

Write which solution you think made the better crystals and why. _____

_____

Light

Objective: Observes how light affects colour.

Materials

- Motivate – Variety of rainbow pictures
- Experience — Each pupil will need: coloured pencils/felt-tip pens/crayons, scissors, sheet of card, glue, pin

▼ Motivate

- Show a variety of rainbow pictures to the pupils. Ask them to share what they see. When do we usually see a rainbow?

- Pose the questions: Where is the sun when you see a rainbow? Did you know that you only see a rainbow if you are standing in between the rain and the light source (sun)?

- Ask pupils: 'If there were five people in a group and a rainbow was visible, would everyone see the same rainbow?' Discuss responses. Generally, no two people see the rainbow in exactly the same way due to the different angles of their positions.

▼ Experience

- Pupils follow the instructions to make and use the colour wheel.

- Discuss observations and allow pupils to record their thoughts and experiences.

- Share the explanation from this page with pupils before they complete the final question on the worksheet.

▼ Explain

- Discuss with pupils how water affects light to form a rainbow.

- Light makes all things visible. All colour depends on light and the amount of light available. All the colours in the visible spectrum combine to produce a light that is colourless or white.

- The colours of the visible spectrum are red, orange, yellow, green, blue, indigo (dark blue), violet (purple). A simple acronym to remember the colours of the rainbow is ROY G BIV.

Rainbow

Definition: noun – a bow or arc of prismatic colours appearing in the sky opposite the sun, due to the refraction and reflection of the sun's rays in drops of rain. (Macquarie online dictionary).

Sunlight is refracted (bent) as it enters a raindrop. Some light is reflected back into the raindrop. As the light leaves the raindrop, it is reflected again at various degrees to form the spectrum. Violet is bent the most at around 40°, while red is bent the least at around 42°. Other colours are bent at regular intervals in between. This is why the colours of the spectrum always appear in the same order.

▼ Apply

- Make your own colour spectrum: Fill a clean glass with water and position it so sunlight passes through to produce a spectrum on the wall. Why do think this happens?

▼ Review and reflect

- Pupils complete the science report on page xii to explain the process they undertook and what the outcome was.

Light

You will need

coloured pencils/
marker pens/crayons

scissors

sheet of card

glue

pin

Task: To observe how light affects colour.

▶ What to do:

1. Colour the sections of the colour wheel using these colours:

   | red   orange   yellow   green   blue   indigo   violet |

2. Cut out the wheel along the dotted line.

3. Glue the wheel onto the card.

4. Cut out the wheel around the card.

5. Poke a pin through the centre of the wheel and spin.

Now that you have made the wheel, think about these questions.

▶ What happened?

When the wheel is spinning, what colour can you see? _____

▶ What I've learned

1. Why do you think this happens? _____

An object appears a certain colour because it reflects only that coloured light. So blue appears blue, because it reflects all the blue from the light.

2. Tell which colour or colours is/are reflected to make these colours.

   (a) yellow _____

   (b) green _____

   (c) white _____

   (d) red _____

   (e) violet _____

   (f) black _____

   (g) indigo _____

   (h) orange _____

   (i) blue _____

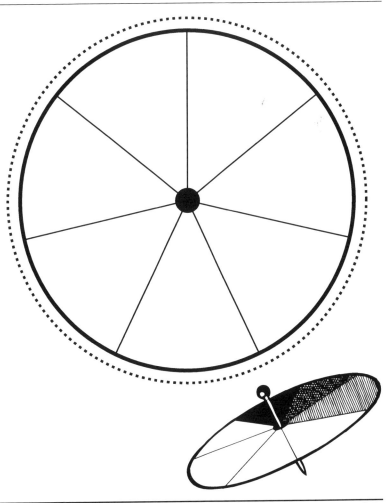

Heat

Objective: Observes the effect heat has on a liquid.

Materials

- Motivate – 3 buckets (one with ice-water, one with tepid water and one with hot water)
- Experience – 2 plastic cups per group, ice-water, hot tap-water, blue and yellow food colouring

▼ Motivate

- Invite pupils to place one hand in the ice-water and one hand in the tepid water. Which hand feels warmer?
- Then invite pupils to place one hand in the tepid water and one hand in the hot water. Which hand feels warmer?
- Discuss how the tepid water felt hot the first time but felt cool the second time. Invite pupils to offer their own suggestions for why this happened.

▼ Experience

- Organise the class into groups of three or four.
- Read through the text at the top of the page. Discuss this idea with pupils. It is a difficult concept to understand that matter is made up of molecules and that the molecules actually move around. Even in a solid object, they vibrate in fixed positions.
- Complete the activity. Be sure to instruct pupils to be careful with the hot water.

> **Safety note:** Hot water should not be so hot that it burns. Remind pupils to be cautious when touching hot water.

- Ensure pupils record their predictions before adding the food colouring to the water.
- Pupils discuss observations and thoughts within the group and then share with the class.

▼ Explain

- Discuss how heat affects water with pupils.

> *Heat is caused by:*
> - *light*
> - *a chemical reaction*
> - *electrical resistance*
> - *friction*
>
> *When water is heated, the molecules that make up the water move faster and more freely. This is why the food colouring moves around and mixes more quickly within the hot water.*

▼ Apply

- Making jelly is an ideal way to observe how temperature changes liquid. Pupils observe how cooling the liquid changes the jelly from a liquid to a solid.
- Melting ice or ice-cream is another way to observe how temperature causes change. Pupils observe how heating a solid changes it from a solid to a liquid.

▼ Review and reflect

- Pupils complete the science recount on page xiii.

Heat

Task: To observe the effect heat has on a liquid.

You will need

2 plastic cups

ice-water

hot tap-water

blue and yellow food colouring

Gases, liquids and solids are all made up of molecules. All molecules are constantly moving, some just move more than others. The more movement molecules have the more heat they produce. The molecules that make up gas are moving really fast and have a lot of space in between each molecule. The molecules that make up a solid barely move and have very little or no space in between.

▶ What will happen?

Predict what you think will happen when you, very gently, add one drop of yellow food colouring and one drop of blue food colouring to cups of iced and hot water.

Prediction

▶ What to do:

1. Take one cup and fill it three-quarters full of ice-water. Take the other cup and fill it three-quarters full of hot tap-water. **Be careful when working with hot water!**

2. Now, very gently, add the colour to each cup.

Now that you have added the colour to the cups complete these questions.

▶ What happened?

What did you observe?

▶ What I've learned

1. Why do you think this happened?

2. What do you think would happen if the water was only warm?

String phones

Objective: Makes and experiments with string phones to explore how sound travels.

Materials

- For each pair of pupils: 2 identical plastic cups; 2 identical paper cups; 2 identical small, medium and large tins (6 in total), with a hole punched in the bottom of each tin; 5 three-metre lengths of string; a drawing-pin

- The small tins and the plastic and paper cups should be approximately the same size.

- Teachers will need to pierce a small hole in the bottom of the tins (this could be done by hammering a nail into each tin) before this activity is presented to the pupils.

▼ Motivate

- Play a music CD and ask the pupils how they think the sound travelled from the CD to our ears. Explain that sound is a form of energy that travels in waves, through objects, to reach our ears. The vibrations are transmitted through the air or other material. Beat on a drum that has grains of rice or paperclips on the top. The pupils can see the vibrations that make the rice or paperclips jump. The pupils can also press a hand against their throat to feel soundwaves travelling through their vocal cords. Discuss with pupils whether they think that sound would travel better through the air or through a solid.

▼ Experience

- Organise the pupils into pairs and distribute the materials. Demonstrate how to make the string phones by threading a piece of string through the holes in a pair of tins and knotting both ends. The pupils can then use the drawing-pin to make a small hole in the bottom of each pair of cups and knot the string through each pair. Show the pupils how they should speak into the tin or cup and hold it to their ear to hear their partner speak at the other end of the string.

- Have the pupils discuss and make predictions with their partner, noting them on the worksheet.

- Read through each of the test instructions with the pupils. They should decide on the same few sentences to say to each other on each phone—speaking for the first time in a whisper and the second in a normal speaking voice. He/She should then circle a number to indicate the volume level and vocal clarity they heard from their partner, with 5 being the best score. Ensure the pupils understand which phone(s) they should use in each test.

▼ Explain

- Explain to the pupils that we hear sounds when energy, in the form of vibrations, hit our ears. Sounds can travel through gases, solids and liquids, but travel through solids the best. A string phone works because the sound vibrates across the taut string to the other tin or cup, where it travels into the ear, vibrating the eardrum.

- A picture of soundwaves could be drawn to show the pupils.

> Sound is a form of energy that travels in invisible waves. We hear sounds when vibrations travel to our ears. The bigger the vibration, the bigger the sound. The bigger the sound, the more sound energy. Pitch is determined by the frequency of the vibration. High-pitched sounds are made by rapid vibrations and low-pitched sounds by slower vibrations. The less space there is for the soundwaves to travel through, the more rapid the waves are and the higher the sound.
>
> Sounds can travel through all kinds of materials; like stone, brick, water and glass. However, some materials prevent sounds from travelling to our ears. Sounds cannot travel through a vacuum because there is nothing to vibrate.

▼ Apply

- Pupils can experiment with other materials to make the best string phone they can; e.g. trying strings of different thicknesses.

▼ Review and reflect

- Pupils complete the science recount, on page xiii, to explain how they made and used their string phones.

▼ Answers

- The pupils should discover that the string needs to be taut to transmit any sound; that tin cups make the best mouthpieces (metal is the best conductor) and that the large tins transmit the best sound (the larger tins amplify the sound).

String phones

Task: To explore how sound travels by experimenting with string phones.

You will need

2 identical plastic cups

2 identical paper cups

2 identical small, medium and large tins (6 in total), with a hole in the bottom of each tin

5 three-metre lengths of string

drawing-pin

▶ What to do:

1. Make five different string phones using the materials listed.

2. Make predictions and then test your phones with a partner.

▶ What will happen?

Do you think a string phone will work better:

(a) if the string is taut or loose? _____

(b) if you use tin cans, plastic cups or paper cups as mouthpieces?

_____

(c) if you use small, medium or large tins as mouthpieces?

_____

▶ What happened?

	Whisper	Normal
Test 1 (Use your small tin phone only)		
Loose string	1 2 3 4 5	1 2 3 4 5
Taut string	1 2 3 4 5	1 2 3 4 5
Test 2 (Use your small tin, plastic and paper phones)		
Tin	1 2 3 4 5	1 2 3 4 5
Plastic	1 2 3 4 5	1 2 3 4 5
Paper	1 2 3 4 5	1 2 3 4 5
Test 3 (Use your three different tin phones)		
Small	1 2 3 4 5	1 2 3 4 5
Medium	1 2 3 4 5	1 2 3 4 5
Large	1 2 3 4 5	1 2 3 4 5

▶ What I've learned

What materials were used to make the best string telephone?
Why do you think this might be?

_____

_____

Conducting materials

Objectives: • Completes an electrical circuit.
• Tests a range of materials for electrical conductivity.

Materials

• electrical equipment: wires with crocodile clips, bulbs, buzzers, switches, batteries, battery holders, selection of materials to test (Choose about six samples, at least half of which will conduct electricity.)

▼ Motivate

• Give examples of where electrical circuits are used in the home. (Light switches, electrical goods, security alarms, air-conditioning units)

• Ask: How can we discover whether or not a material conducts electricity?

• Ask: What sort of materials conduct electricity?

• Ask: Why is the property of electrical conductivity important?

▼ Experience

• Pupils follow the procedure and determine which materials can conduct electricity.

• Materials that are conductors of electricity will complete the electrical circuit. Those that are not conductors—i.e. insulators—will not complete the circuit and the light or buzzer will not work.

• Pupils will notice that stronger conductors will produce a louder buzz or brighter light than a weaker conductor.

▼ Explain

• Pupils explain what happened by completing the 'What I've learned' section.

> Circuits need to be complete if they are to work. The wires must go in a loop from the power source and back again. Electricity cannot travel around an incomplete circuit. All batteries in the circuit must be connected facing the same direction.
>
> Most conductors are metals—e.g. steel, copper, iron, gold, silver—but graphite, a type of carbon which is used in pencils, is also a conductor of electricity.
>
> Insulators, such as plastics, rubber, glass and wood, do not allow the passage of electricity.
>
> Copper is a metal used in electrical wires. Plastic is the insulating material used to cover the wires to prevent electricity passing to objects which may touch the wires.

▼ Apply

• Pupils draw circuit pictures (rather than diagrams) for different electrical appliances in the home.

▼ Review and reflect

• Pupils consider how they could determine the relative strength of each conducting material. (Observation, by comparing strength of light from bulb or sound from buzzer.)

• Pupils consider what type of material could be used to insulate electricity (for use in cables and switch covers) to protect from electrical current.

• Pupils design a fair test to determine if the size of conducting material affects the strength of the electrical current supplying the bulb or buzzer.

▼ Answers

What happened?

1. Some materials conduct electricity.

2. Other materials do not conduct electricity.

Conducting materials

Task: To classify materials as conductors or non-conductors of electricity.

What to do:

1. Construct an electrical circuit, including a buzzer or light bulb and a switch.

2. Check that the buzzer or light bulb works when the switch is activated to complete the circuit.

3. Draw and label the circuit. Include the purpose of each part.

4. Remove the switch from the circuit and replace it, in turn, with each sample material.

You will need

electrical equipment:

wires with crocodile clips

bulbs

buzzers

switches

batteries

battery holders

selection of materials to test

What happened?

1. Complete the sentences.

   (a) Some materials _____ .

   (b) Other materials _____ .

2. Write each material in the correct column in the table.

Conductor	Non-conductor

What I've learned

Explain in one sentence what this activity has shown.

_____

_____

Matchbox in motion

Objective: Tests a variety of materials to see how effectively they slow down an object in motion.

Materials

- Matchbox; metre ruler; different surfaces such as flat metal sheet, wooden chopping board, fabric, carpet, rubber, sandpaper, bubble wrap, cardboard etc.

▼ Motivate

- Ask pupils: If you slide your eraser across the table, what happens? (It eventually stops.) Why does it stop?

- Ask: If you rub your hands together, what can you feel? (Heat) Why?

- Ask: When you are walking in your trainers on wet pavement, why don't you slip over? (Grip on sole of trainers.)

▼ Experience

- Organise the pupils into groups and distribute the materials.

- Read the worksheet with the class. Why is it important that the experiment is a 'fair test'? Give pupils time to discuss how the experiment can be a fair test. Suggestion: The same group member pushes the matchbox each time to ensure the same strength of force is used.

- Pupils share their predictions with the class and give reasons for their ranking.

- Pupils follow the procedure on the worksheet to complete the experiment.

- Discuss with pupils if the results were different from, or the same as, their predictions.

▼ Explain

- Discuss the force known as friction with the class. Explain that friction is a force that acts against a moving object. The friction between the bottom of the matchbox and the surface material causes the matchbox to slow down or stop.

- Pupils write their conclusions about what they have learned.

The force that occurs when two objects or surfaces are moving against each other is called friction. Friction is a force that resists motion. It always acts in the opposite direction to the motion and occurs because of the bumps on the surfaces of two objects. Even the smoothest of surfaces provide friction.

When two objects move together and there is friction, they lose energy and slow down or stop moving. The energy changes from kinetic energy (moving energy) to heat energy. This is why when we rub our hands together, we feel heat.

Many machines use a lubrication to reduce the heat created when parts are sliding against one another (such as oil in a car engine).

▼ Apply

- As a class, discuss where friction is used during a tennis match.

- Pupils choose another sport and work in groups to record where friction occurs. Pupils draw a diagram of the game and label the areas showing where friction occurs.

- A scientific diagram framework is located on page xvi.

▼ Review and reflect

- Pupils complete the science recount on page xiii about their 'Matchbox in motion' experiment.

Matchbox in motion

Task: To test five different materials to see which one will slow down or stop a matchbox in motion.

You will need

matchbox

metre ruler

different surfaces such as fabric, carpet, rubber, sandpaper, metal sheet, wood, bubble wrap, cardboard etc.

What to do:

1. Write your predictions in the table below.

2. Place the metre ruler flat on the surface you are testing.

3. Place the matchbox next to the start of the ruler and push it.

4. Measure the distance it travels.

5. Test each material three times and complete the results table below.

What will happen?

List and number the materials from 1 to 5. 1 being the surface you think the matchbox will travel the shortest distance on and 5 being the surface you think the matchbox will travel the furthest distance on.

Surface material	Rank (1–5)

What happened?

Check your predictions by pushing the matchbox across each of the different surfaces three times. Record your results.

Surface material	Distance travelled (cm)		
	Test 1	Test 2	Test 3

What I've learned

Write a sentence that sums up your findings about objects moving across different surfaces.

_____

_____

Magnetic robot

Objective: Recognises magnetic and non-magnetic materials.

Materials

- 16 plastic cups, string, 4 strong bar magnets, barbecue skewer (safety first!), sticky tape, selection of materials; include metals and non-metals, magnetic metals and non-magnetic metals

▼ Motivate

- Ask pupils to list which materials they think are attracted to magnets.
- Ask: 'How can we test which materials are magnetic?'
- Ask: 'Are all metals magnetic?'

▼ Experience

- Pupils follow the procedure to make their plastic cup robots. They may find attaching the pots with string challenging. Knotting the string will prevent the pots sliding into each other. Separate lengths of string will be required for the head and torso, the arms and each leg. Magnets can be secured to the string with tape to prevent them from slipping from their ties.

▼ Explain

- The robot will pick up magnetic materials but not non-magnetic materials. The samples can then be classified into the appropriate group.

When magnets are placed near one another, they will either attract or repel. When magnets are placed near a magnetic material, they will attract that material but not repel it.

Materials that are not metal are not magnetic. Not all metals are magnetic.

Only iron and some iron alloys (steel, cobalt and nickel) are magnetic. Some stainless steels are not magnetic. Some coins are magnetic as they have a thin coating of copper over a steel core.

Aluminium cans—those that crush easily—are not magnetic. Drink cans are generally made from aluminium.

Tins used for food products are mostly made from iron and, therefore, are magnetic.

▼ Apply

- Pupils could use their robots to identify magnetic objects around the classroom and school environment. Having established which objects are magnetic, these could be further classified into different types of metal.

▼ Review and reflect

- Pupils write a report describing how they used the robot to classify different materials; including suggestions for how the robot may be used in a rubbish recycling project.

▼ Answers

What happened?

1. The recycling robot picked up magnetic materials.
2. The recycling robot did not pick up non-magnetic materials.

What I've learned

1. magnetic   2. attracted   3. not   4. metals

Magnetic robot

Task: To make a recycling robot.	

You will need

16 plastic cups

string

4 strong bar magnets

barbecue skewer
(Safety first!)

sticky tape

selection of materials
to test

What to do:

1. Using string, knotted at intervals, make a 'robot' by connecting the plastic cups as shown below.

2. Stick a magnet to the feet and hands of the robot.

3. Allow the robot to bend over each sample so that its hands and feet are all touching the sample.

4. Lift the robot.

5. Identify the magnetic and non-magnetic materials and list them in the appropriate place in the table below.

Magnetic	Non-magnetic
The robot picked up:	The robot did not pick up:
_____	_____
_____	_____
_____	_____
_____	_____

What happened?

Complete the sentences.

(a) The recycling robot picked up _____

_____.

(b) The recycling robot did not pick up _____

_____.

What I've learned

Fill the gaps using words from the box.

not   magnetic   metals   attracted

Some materials are _____[1]. This means that magnets are

_____[2] to them. Non-metals are _____[3] magnetic.

Not all _____[4] are magnetic.

Confectionery catapult

Objective: Constructs a simple machine that uses elastic power to launch a sweet.

Materials

- 300 mL milk carton, 3 elastic bands (have different sizes available), toothpick, 2 pencils, matchbox, sticky tape, small sweets (like mini-marshmallows or small mints)

▼ Motivate

Safety note: Be careful when letting go of elastic bands as they can snap and cause pain.

- Stretch an elastic band. What does it do? Let it go (carefully). What does it do?

- When stretched, the elastic band became long and thin. It changed its shape. When it was let go, it returned to its original shape.

- Squash a rubber ball. It springs back to its original shape without any damage.

▼ Experience

- Pupils follow the procedure to construct their Confectionery catapults.

- Once constructed, pupils test the launcher a number of times until it works properly.

- Line the Confectionery catapults up on the edge of a table and place a bucket about three metres away. Which group can land their sweets in the bucket?

▼ Explain

- Provide pupils with the explanation before they complete 'What I've learned'.

> If an elastic band (or spring) is stretched, it pulls on whatever is stretching it. If a spring is compressed, it pushes on whatever is compressing it. Forces act in particular directions. A big push on an object will move it in the direction of the push. Elastic materials are good at storing and releasing energy. Steel and rubber can both be very elastic. Steel can be made into springs, and rubber into elastic bands. Some of the more elastic materials found in nature include tendon, horn, resin and different types of wood.
>
> Even elastic materials have their limit. Bend a bow too far and it will break. Stretch a rubber band too far and it will snap. Squash a rubber ball too hard and it will crumble. This means that the materials have reached their 'elastic limit'.

▼ Apply

- Challenge the pupils to use the same principles to propel a toy car along a flat surface. Groups can compete to see who can make the car go the furthest. Use a meter ruler to measure the distances.

▼ Review and reflect

- Pupils reflect on the confectionery catapult activity by completing the science reflection on page xi.

▼ Answers

What I've learned

1. storing   2. releasing   3. force   4. further

Confectionery catapult

Task: To construct a machine that will launch a sweet into a bucket.

You will need

300 mL milk carton

3 elastic bands of different sizes

toothpick

2 pencils

sticky tape

matchbox

small sweet

What to do:

1. Cut the top off the milk carton, then cut the carton as show in Diagram 1.

2. Punch a hole in each side and one through the back of the carton.

3. Push an elastic band through the hole in the back and hold it in place with a toothpick. Push a pencil through the holes in the sides (see Diagram 2).

4. Cut the tray of a match box in half lengthwise. Tape it to the point of the second pencil.

5. Lay the second pencil on the horizontal pencil, with the blunt end facing the front of your confectionery catapult (see Diagram 3).

6. Loop the elastic band **UNDER** the horizontal pencil and then **OVER** the blunt end of the second pencil (see Diagram 4).

7. Tape the top flap at the front of the carton down so it is flat.

8. Place a sweet in the matchbox tray. Pull back the pencil and release your sweet.

9. Adjust your confectionery catapult to make it work better. You may want to try using elastic bands of various sizes.

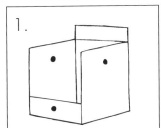 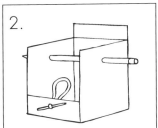 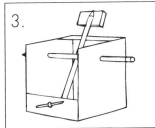 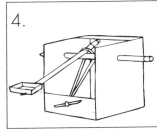

What happened?

Describe how your confectionery catapult performed and how you improved it to make it work better.

_____

_____

_____

What I've learned

Complete the sentences.

releasing	further	storing	force

Elastic materials are very good at _____¹ and _____² energy.

The bigger the _____³ applied, the _____⁴ the sweet will travel.

Make a sun catcher

Objective: Plans, designs and makes a sun catcher that uses the sun's heat to warm the air inside.

Materials

- Different types of containers, thermometers, stopwatches or timers.

- Materials for pupils to choose from for their designs, such as tissue paper, aluminium foil, black paper and card, large sheet of stiff paper, plastic cling wrap, sticky tape

▼ Motivate

- Ask pupils: How do we heat our homes and the school? Discuss.

- Ask pupils if there is a way we could heat our homes using an energy source that isn't a fossil fuel (coal, gas or oil).

- Ask: What about solar energy? What is solar energy? Where do we see it being used?

▼ Experience

- Pupils follow the steps to plan, design and make a sun catcher.

Points to note:

- The inside of the sun catcher should be black to absorb the light and heat. It could be lined with black paper.

- Cling wrap can be used to cover the container. A hole needs to be made for the thermometer. If tape is placed around the hole, it will be easier to remove and replace the thermometer when checking the temperature.

▼ Explain

- Provide pupils with the explanation below before they complete the 'What I've learned' section.

> The sun's rays bring large amounts of light to the Earth. This light is converted to retain energy within the Earth's atmosphere, which holds much of the heat. Energy from the sun is called solar energy. This energy can be converted to other forms of energy to warm our surroundings, our homes and ourselves.
>
> Non-renewable energy sources (the fossil fuels—oil, coal and gas) are energy sources that are going to, eventually, run out.
>
> Renewable energy sources (solar, wind, water, tidal, wave, geothermal, biomass etc.) are created naturally and can replace themselves (which means they are sustainable).

▼ Apply

- Pupils discuss ways they could transform their sun catcher into a solar oven. Pupils use the science investigation framework on page xiv to plan their changes. Ask: What types of food would cook best in a solar oven?

▼ Review and reflect

- Pupils complete the science recount on page xiii in relation to designing and making the sun catcher.

- Use a camera to photograph the pupils making their sun catchers and display the photos on a board near the sun catchers and the pupils' recounts.

▼ Answers

What I've learned

Possible answer: As the cost involved in heating and cooling a home is the largest part of an energy bill, using renewable energy sources to heat and cool can reduce these costs greatly. The aim is to keep the air inside the house cool during summer and warm in winter. People should choose materials when building their home that will do this. Also, try to keep the summer sun out by having overhanging roofs and planting trees by windows, and position the house so the low winter sun can shine through the windows.

Make a sun catcher

Task: To design and make a sun catcher that will trap the sun's heat and warm the air inside.

▶ What to do:

1. Follow the steps to help you design a sun catcher. Tick each step as you complete it.

   ☐ Choose a container such as a cereal box, yoghurt pot, milk carton, shoe box etc.

   ☐ With your group, discuss how you can increase the temperature of the air inside your sun catcher.

   ☐ Which type of material can you use to line the inside surface of your sun catcher so it will absorb the most sunlight?

   ☐ Choose a transparent material to cover the opening of your sun catcher that will allow the sun to shine through.

   ☐ How will you measure if the temperature inside your sun catcher has changed? (Remember, you need to be able to read the temperature quickly and with little disturbance to your sun catcher.)

   ☐ How will you help the heat to stay trapped inside your sun catcher?

   ☐ Where will you position your sun catcher to capture the most heat?

2. Once the decisions about your sun catcher have been made, draw your design neatly and accurately on a separate sheet of paper. Remember to label all of the materials used in your design.

3. Construct your sun catcher and test it on a sunny day.

▶ What happened?

Record your results in the table below.

Time (minutes)	0									
Temperature (° Celsius)										

▶ What I've learned

Explain how this experiment can help us to design energy-friendly homes.

_____

_____

_____

Energy-friendly vehicle

Objective: Plans and designs a sustainable (energy-friendly) mode of transport.

Materials

Note: Check the designs and materials required before the pupils begin making their models as some materials may need to be ordered.

- Art paper, pencils, ruler
- Access to the library and Internet (optional)

Motivate

- Ask the pupils to close their eyes and imagine how they will be travelling to work or to visit friends in 50 year's time. Listen to their ideas. Choose a few ideas and ask the pupils how their vehicles will be powered. Will it be by petrol? Gas? Something else?

Experience

Note: An understanding of non-renewable and renewable energy sources would be an advantage prior to this lesson.

- List the non-renewable energy sources (the fossil fuels—oil, coal and gas) on the board. Explain that non-renewable energy is energy that comes from the fossil fuels which are, eventually, going to run out.

- List renewable energy sources on the board (solar, wind, water, tidal, wave, geothermal, biomass etc.) and explain that renewable energy means it occurs naturally and replaces itself.

- Organise pupils into small groups. Pupils plan and design an energy-friendly vehicle that uses one or more renewable energy sources.

Note: Pupils may wish to redraw their design sketch neatly and accurately onto large art paper. All materials and parts should be labelled.

Explain

- Each group shows its design and vehicle to the class and explains what it is, how it works and why it is environmentally friendly.

> People have used renewable energy sources for transportation for thousands of years—walking, riding on animals (such as horses, donkeys and camels) and travelling in sail boats. Less than 200 years ago, people started to use fossil fuels for transportation. These fuels are non-renewable so they will eventually run out. They also cause pollution.

Apply

- Ask pupils to design a house that is powered completely by renewable energy sources. Is it possible?

Review and reflect

- After viewing all groups' models, pupils discuss and record how they could improve their model.

- Pupils complete the science reflection framework on page xi, commenting on how their group worked together.

Energy-friendly vehicle

Task: To invent an energy-friendly future mode of transport powered by one or more renewable energy sources.

▶ **What to do:**

1. Complete the plan for your vehicle below.

Design brief

Group members:

Design purpose:

Initial ideas:

Renewable energy used:

☐ solar energy

☐ wind energy

☐ hydro (water) power

☐ wave energy

☐ other _____

Design sketch: (with labels showing materials used)

How will it work?

2. Construct your futuristic vehicle.

▶ **What I've learned**

Present your vehicle to the class and explain how it is energy-friendly.

What do seeds need to grow?

Objective: Tests and observes eight different growing conditions and decides which condition is best for optimum seed germination.

Materials

- For each pupil: 1 broad bean seed (soaked in water overnight), clear plastic cup, sticky labels, 3 paper towels
- For the class: 4 clear tanks, 4 tank dividers, 1 tank light, measuring cups, sticky labels, digital camera, copies of Science journal framework (page xv)

▼ Motivate

- Show a variety of seeds to the pupils. Allow them to feel and observe them closely: What do they notice? Discuss how each looks and feels.

- Ask pupils: 'What do you think this seed needs in order to grow into a plant?' Record responses.

▼ Experience

To prepare a seed

- Give each pupil a clear plastic cup, label, three paper towels and a soaked bean.

- Each pupil writes his/her name on the label and attaches it to the cup.

- Line the inside of the cup with one sheet of paper towel folded in half. Scrunch up the other two pieces and push them into the middle of the cup to hold the lining secure.

- Place the seed securely between the plastic cup and the lining sheet of paper towel.

- Set up the experiment as per the guidelines on page 39.

Watering

- As a class, decide on a standard amount of water to be used; e.g. 50 mL every second day. Therefore, the calculation for 2 x water would either be to use 50 mL water every day or 100 mL water every second day and 0.5 x water would either be to use 50 mL water every four days or 25 mL water every second day. These measures must be consistent for the test to be fair.

  Note: Watering should occur at the same time each day.

- Distribute the science journal worksheet on page xv, to all pupils. Pupils draw diagrams to show the changes in the seed and record any significant data or observations. Two or three copies of the journal are required, depending on the number of days the seeds are observed.

- Use a digital camera at regular intervals to show the seed growth. A daily photo could be compiled into a computer presentation at the end of the experiment to show seed germination in the form of a time line.

▼ Explain

- Discuss the results of the experiment and the essential requirements plants need for optimum growth and why they are necessary.

> Seeds come in a great variety of sizes, shapes and colours. Every seed contains a tiny plant (an embryo), with leaf, stem and root parts, waiting for the right conditions (usually warmth, moisture and oxygen) to germinate and grow.
>
> Seeds contain food supplies (cotyledons) the embryo needs for growth. When the seed is exposed to the appropriate conditions, the embryo cell starts to absorb water and expands. The seed coating breaks open and roots and shoots start to emerge. The shoot develops leaves and stems.

- The bean growth activity allows pupils to observe the germination process and the changes in the seed without the seed being concealed in soil. The seeds in this activity will germinate and grow for a short time, thriving on the food supply stored in the cotyledons. Eventually the seeds will need soil to continue their growth and plants can be transferred to soil, if desired.

▼ Apply

- Some plants need a great deal of water while others only require a small amount of water to grow best. Find out what types of plants fit into these categories: Where are they found? What other conditions do they need to thrive?

- Pupils work in small groups to research and report information discovered about different growing conditions for plants.

▼ Review and reflect

- Discuss the outcome in small groups: Was it as expected? Why or why not? What are the optimum conditions for seed germination? What else could be tested if the experiment was repeated?

What do seeds need to grow?

Task: To test and observe eight different growing conditions and decide which condition is best for seed germination.

You will need

tanks

tank dividers

tank light

sticky labels

measuring cups

clear plastic cup

3 paper towels

1 broad bean which has been soaked overnight

sticky labels

digital camera

▶ What to do:

As a class, follow these instructions to prepare your seeds:

(a) Set up each tank like the diagrams below. Attach labels to the front of each tank.

(b) Place at least one seed in each area of the tanks.

(c) Record your observations, ongoing data (including length measurements) and sketches in your science journal for 10 to 14 days.

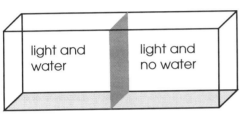

Tank 1: on windowsill

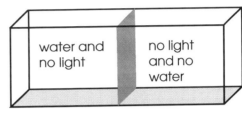

Tank 2: in cupboard

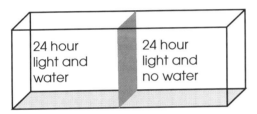

Tank 3: in cupboard with light

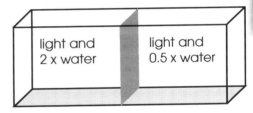

Tank 4: on windowsill

▶ What will happen?

1. Colour the section of the tank you think is best for seed growth GREEN.

2. Colour the section of the tank you think will not allow seed growth RED.

▶ What happened?

1. The seed in the tank placed _____ with the conditions

_____ grew the best.

2. The seed in the tank placed _____ with the conditions

_____ grew the least.

▶ What I've learned

The best conditions for a seed to germinate and grow are _____

_____

_____

How to grow tasty tomatoes

Objective: Finds the best method for growing the tastiest tomatoes.

Materials:

- fresh tomatoes, tomato plants, pots, potting mix, mask, gloves, garden stakes and ties, sticky labels, fertiliser, digital camera, copies of science journal on page xv

▼ Motivate

- Cut up some juicy, ripe tomatoes and share them with the class. Be sure to include several varieties.

  Safety note: Ensure the tomatoes, utensils, work space and pupils' hands are thoroughly washed before eating!

- Ask the pupils which one they liked best. Why? Discuss the colour, size and aroma, as well as the taste and texture.

- Ask: 'What makes a tomato tasty?' This needs to be clarified within the class as it is important to have a consistent idea of what constitutes a good tasting tomato.

▼ Experience

- Organise pupils into pairs and distribute materials.

- Follow the worksheet to set up the experiment.

- Discuss why it is important to keep one plant as the 'norm' and use the other plant to trial different approaches to improving growth. This allows us to see whether or not our approach works.

- Different approaches pupils may choose could include: using fertiliser at regular intervals during the growing; trimming the leaves to make the plant bushier; talking to the plant; playing music to the plant etc.

  Safety note: Ensure when fertiliser and potting mix are used that pupils wear gloves and masks and wash their hands thoroughly afterwards.

- Pupils will also need to maintain a science journal (use page xv) throughout the experiment to record their observations.

▼ Explain

- Discuss with pupils the different approaches farmers use to grow the best crop of tomatoes.

Tomato plants don't respond well to sitting in water, so it is important to make sure the pot is well-drained. It is also important to water the base of the plant without wetting the leaves as tomato plants tend to burn easily when wet. Be sure not to let the plant dry out. The use of mulch may be helpful to retain moisture.

Tomato plants must receive at least six hours of sunlight each day, so be sure to locate the pots in a position that receives full sunlight. More sun equals more fruit. Less sun equals lots of lovely green foliage, but not a lot of fruit.

A regular fortnightly feed of liquid fertiliser will encourage the seedling to form flowers and resist disease.

Pruning is not essential, however, light pruning will reduce the number of fruit but the fruit will be larger. Never remove leaves from the plant once it has fruit. This will expose the fruit to direct sunlight and cause it to burn.

▼ Apply

- Discuss and research growing tomatoes the traditional way and growing them hydroponically: What are the differences? What are the benefits? Pupils can set up a hydroponic system at the same time as the traditional experiment to observe the differences.

▼ Review and reflect

- Pupils complete a science reflection sheet (see page xi) for their tomato growing experiment.

How to grow tasty tomatoes

Task: To find the best method for growing the tastiest tomatoes.

You will need

tomato plants

pots

potting mix

mask

gloves

garden stakes and ties

sticky labels

fertiliser

What will happen?

1. Using the experiment on broad beans, you learnt what a seed needs in order for it to germinate. What do you think a plant requires for it to grow?

2. What special treatment do you think it would take to grow a tomato plant so it produces the tastiest tomatoes possible?

What to do:

1. Work with a partner to set up two tomato plants in pots. Label each with your names. One plant will receive basic care: sunlight and water. Label this one 'basic'. The other will receive the special treatment you think it will need to produce the tastiest tomatoes. Label this one 'special'.

2. Record the initial measurements of each plant in the table below.

3. Care for and monitor both plants according to their requirements. Regularly record observations in your science journal using keywords, measures and diagrams or photos.

4. After an agreed period of time, record the final measurements of each plant in the table below.

	Basic		Special	
	Initial	Final	Initial	Final
Height of stem				
Number of leaves				
Number of flowers				
Number of fruit				

What I've learned

How do the results compare?

Life cycle of a flowering plant

Objective: Records in pictures the life cycle of a flowering plant.

Materials

- 6 labels (seed, germinated seed, seed with first root and first shoot, seedling, flowering plant, fruiting plant), 6 sheets of blank A4 paper, scissors, split pins and pencils
- Photocopy the pupil page onto card for extra strength.

▼ Motivate

- Organise the pupils into six groups. Give each group one of these life cycle labels: *seed, germinated seed, seed with first root and first shoot, seedling, flowering plant, fruiting plant*, and an A4 sheet of blank paper.
- Each group is responsible for drawing a diagram to show the stage of the life cycle they were given. Diagrams must be labelled and supported by a simple statement about the changes that occur at that stage.
- Display the A4 sheets on a board in the appropriate order to show the life cycle stages.
- Discuss the cycle and what happens at each stage. Identify the changes that occur to that plant.

▼ Experience

- Distribute and read the worksheet. Pupils discuss in pairs the flowering plant they would like to represent on the life cycle wheel. For the purposes of this activity, it is recommended pupils select a plant which reproduces from a seed.
- Pupils follow the instructions to complete the life cycle wheel.
- Swap life cycle wheels with other groups to view the life cycle of different plants.

▼ Explain

- Discuss the life cycle of flowering plants with pupils.

Plants can reproduce from seeds, spores or by using parts of the plant itself (e.g. stem cuttings). Most produce seeds that can be dispersed by the wind, people, water or animals. When the seeds have the right conditions to grow (space, food, water, light), they start to germinate.

Once the seedling starts to grow out of the seed it also develops roots. The young plant continues to grow; developing a stem, leaves and, later, bearing flowers and fruits. The flower is the reproductive organ of the plant. Pollination of the flower leads to the making of more seeds and the cycle continues.

Non-flowering plants, such as ferns and mushrooms, reproduce through spores, usually found on the underside of the plant.

▼ Apply

- In small groups, pupils survey plants within the school grounds. Observe each plant carefully and record results in a table similar to this:

	Tally	Places found
Seed		
Seed with first shoots		
Seedling		
Plant in flower		
Plant in fruit		

- Discuss the results: Were there any surprises? Would the results be different at another time of the year?
- Collected data could also be presented in the form of a graph.

▼ Review and reflect

- Pupils work in small groups to create a computer presentation showing the life cycle of a flowering plant.

Life cycle of a flowering plant

Task: To record the life cycle of a flowering plant in pictures.

You will need

scissors

split pins

pencils

▶ What to do – Circle 1

1. Write the title; e.g. 'Life cycle of a bean'.

2. Decorate to suit the chosen plant.

3. Cut along the dotted line.

▶ What to do – Circle 2

1. Draw pictures to show the life cycle of your chosen plant.

2. Colour.

3. Cut along the dotted line.

4. Use a split pin to attach the circles together at the centre point, with Circle 1 on top of Circle 2.

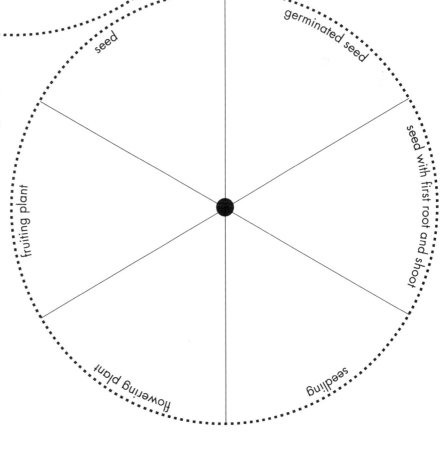

Habitat hunt

Objectives:
- Writes clue for an animal and plays 'The habitat hunt'.
- Considers why an animal lives in its habitat.

Materials

- A4 paper, marker pens, safety pins (two per pupil)

▼ Motivate

- Write three clues on the board and ask pupils to identify the animal; e.g. 'I have feathers. I lay eggs. People eat my eggs. What am I?'
- Ask pupils to describe this animal's habitat.

▼ Experience

- Depending on the background knowledge and interests of the pupils in your class, choose four habitats. Make a list of animals from these habitats so you have one animal per pupil.

  Rainforest: parrot, butterfly, tree frog, monkey, bat

  Desert: lizard, camel, coyote, rattlesnake, kangaroo, dingo, scorpion, desert rat

  Woodland: squirrel, woodpecker, mouse, badger

  Ocean: fish, shark, turtle, whale, dolphin, jellyfish, starfish

  Wetland: swan, frog, pond skater, dragonfly, leech, water snail

- On the board, write the names of the habitats you have chosen (a good distance apart) or, alternatively, write the names on large sheets of paper and attach them to walls in the classroom.

- Allocate each pupil an animal (including insects and birds). Pupils have to write three clues on his/her sheet of paper to describe their animal.

  For example, if a pupil is allocated a crab, he/she may write:

  I have a shell.   *I have claws.*   *I walk sideways.*

- With their descriptions pinned to their chest, pupils walk around the classroom reading the descriptions of other pupils. When they find an animal belonging in the same habitat as theirs, they stay together. (One option would be to have pupils link arms.) When the pupils have formed a group of four, they go to the habitat they belong in. The first correct group to complete its habitat is the winner.

- Pupils complete the worksheet about their animal and its habitats.

- Each group sits at a table together and draws and writes about their habitat. Group members can share their knowledge about the habitat to complete the boxes.

- Pupils may require books or the Internet to help them make notes about the habitat.

▼ Explain

A habitat is the place where organisms live, grow, feed and reproduce. Many animals have special adaptations to give them the best chance of survival in a habitat.

All animals and plants rely on their habitat for water and food, shelter and safety.

There are many different habitats on earth. Some include: wetlands, deserts, woodlands, ocean, rainforest, ponds, trees, flower bed, under a leaf or stone.

▼ Apply

- Allocate a habitat to each pupil. Pupils choose an animal from the habitat and present a brief oral report to the class about why they think the animal is suited to this habitat.

- Pupils complete the worksheet sentence about why the animal lives in that habitat.

  For example:

  The *frog* has *wetlands* as its habitat because *there is plenty of water and damp air so it doesn't dry out, there are lots of insects to eat and water for frog spawn.*

▼ Review and reflect

- Pupils use the information on their worksheet to complete an A4 information poster about their animal and its habitat.

- Pupils complete the science reflection sheet on page xi about the 'Habitat hunt' activity.

Habitat hunt

Tasks: To play a game matching animals to their habitats.
To consider why an animal lives in its habitat.

▶ **What to do:**

1. My animal is _____

   and its habitat is _____

   Other animals from that habitat are

   _____

2. Play the 'Habitat hunt' game.

3. (a) Draw your animal in its habitat below. (b) With your group, make notes about the habitat.

	Climate	Type of food available

| | Materials for shelter | Amount of water |

(c) Other animals from that habitat are:

| | Type of plants | Amount of light |

▶ **What I've learned**

The _____ has _____ as its

habitat because _____

_____

Teeth enemies

Objective: Conducts experiments to gain understanding of how certain foods and drinks effect our teeth.

Materials

- Each group: sticky labels for naming experiments; Task 1: raw egg, glass cup, vinegar, newspaper; Task 2: 2 hard-boiled eggs – shelled, 2 glass cups, water, cola soft drink

Note: Both experiments need to be left overnight.

▼ Motivate

- Make a class list of ways to look after your teeth; for example: brush at least twice daily, floss, use mouth wash regularly, drinks lots of water, visit the dentist regularly, eat the correct foods (not too many sweet things).

▼ Experience

- In groups, pupils complete each task. They set up and label their experiments and leave them overnight.

▼ Explain

- The following day, pupils remove the eggs from the glasses and complete the 'What happened?' and 'What I've learned' sections on the worksheet.

- Discuss what happens to the inside layers of teeth when the enamel is eaten away by acid in the mouth. When the pulp is exposed, a toothache occurs.

Enamel is the thin outer layer of the tooth which protects the tooth pulp and nerve endings inside. Enamel is the hardest substance in human bodies. When food or sweet drinks are left in the mouth after eating or drinking, bacteria eats into the enamel. This bacteria forms a white, sticky slime called plaque which covers the teeth. The plaque contains acid which rots away the tooth enamel, and stains and weakens the teeth. The pulp of the tooth is then exposed. This can cause toothaches and require fillings.

Teeth become visible in babies at about six month's of age. Most children have all their teeth by the time they are three years old. They are called the primary (or baby) teeth and there are 20 of them. As a child grows older, these teeth begin to fall out because they are pushed out of the way by permanent teeth.

▼ Apply

- Pupils design a similar experiment to Task 2 to test which other liquids stain our teeth. Liquids such as coffee, tea, juice and milk could be tested. Pupils construct a table to record their results. The table should also include the control liquid—water.

- Complete the science investigation framework supplied on page xiv.

▼ Review and reflect

- In small groups, pupils write and create a picture book for younger children about a tooth fairy concerned about the state of the teeth she is collecting. The book should be entertaining, but still convey the message that children need to care for their teeth.

Teeth enemies

Task 1: To investigate how acidic food can weaken our teeth and cause tooth decay.

▶ What to do:

1. Place newspaper on the table.

2. Half fill the glass cup with vinegar.

3. Place the raw egg in the vinegar. Add more vinegar if the egg is not covered.

4. Leave the experiment overnight.

▶ What happened?

Remove the egg from the glass cup. How does it look and feel?

_____

_____

▶ What I've learned

Explain how this experiment helps us to understand more about our teeth.

_____

_____

You will need

raw egg

glass cup

vinegar

newspaper

Task 2: To investigate how cola soft drink can stain our teeth.

▶ What to do:

1. Pour cola in a glass cup so it is half full. Add a shelled hard-boiled egg.

2. Pour the same amount of water into the other glass cup and add the second hard-boiled egg.

3. Leave the eggs overnight.

▶ What happened?

Remove the eggs from the glass cups. Describe their appearance.

Egg in water: _____

Egg in cola: _____

▶ What I've learned

Explain how this experiment helps us to understand more about our teeth.

_____

You will need

2 hard-boiled eggs (shelled)

cola soft drink

water

2 glass cups

Where does the blood go?

Objective: Demonstrates (physically) how blood moves through the body.

Materials

- labels for head, heart, lung (x 2), arm (x 2), leg (x 2) and blood (x 2); 10 oxygen tank labels and 10 carbon dioxide tank labels; 10 safety pins to attach labels; big empty space for activity

▼ Motivate

- Ask pupils if they have ever counted their heartbeats. Demonstrate how to read a pulse in order to count heartbeats.

- Pupils count and record their heartbeats while relaxed.

- Pupils perform jump-squats for 30 seconds. Pupils then count and record their heartbeats after the exercise.

- Discuss the difference: Why do you think the number of beats increased?

▼ Experience

- Copy and cut out the labels from the worksheet. Allocate eight children to be a body part— 1 head, 1 heart, 2 lungs, 2 arms, 2 legs. Give each their label and a safety pin to attach it to their shirt.

- Imagine a body flat on the ground that is the size of the room. Position the eight pupils in appropriate positions within the classroom, as if representing the body.

- Photocopy the oxygen tanks five times and give the pupils playing the lungs all 10 oxygen tanks (five each).

- Photocopy the carbon dioxide tanks five times and give the pupils playing the head, arms and legs two carbon dioxide tanks each.

- Choose two pupils to play the blood and give them their labels and safety pins.

  1. The 'blood' begins in the heart. The heart directs the blood to the lungs.

  2. As the blood arrives in the lungs, each pupil is passed an oxygen tank by the pupils playing the lungs.

  3. The blood with the oxygen then travels back to the heart to be directed to a part of the body; e.g. head, arm or leg.

  4. When the blood reaches that part of the body, the blood exchanges their oxygen tank for a carbon dioxide tank with the body part (head, arm or leg). Once given a carbon dioxide tank, the blood makes its way back to the heart which directs it toward the lungs.

  5. The blood exchanges their 'carbon dioxide' for 'oxygen' with the lungs.

  6. The blood travels back to the heart which directs the blood to a different part of the body.

  7. This continues until all body parts have been visited by the blood.

- Repeat the dramatisation of how the circulatory system works several times, making sure each pupil plays the role of the blood and a body part at least once. Allow time for pupils to develop a clear understanding of the cycle.

▼ Explain

- Discuss the role of the circulatory system.

> The circulatory system is responsible for keeping blood moving around the body, which, in turn, supplies oxygen and nutrients to the cells and keeps us healthy. The centre of this system is the heart, which pumps blood continuously. We have around two to four litres of blood (for children) in our body and it takes around 60 seconds to pump blood to every cell. The blood pumped away from the heart is full of oxygen and nutrients ready to be taken to the rest of the body. The blood moving toward the heart is full of carbon dioxide and waste products collected from the rest of the body. At the lungs, the carbon dioxide is discharged and fresh oxygen collected.

▼ Apply

- Pupils write a paragraph summarising the circulatory system; including how and why the blood travels around the body and the main purpose of the heart and lungs.

- Pupils consider how an asthma attack would affect the circulatory system.

▼ Review and reflect

- Pupils complete the science recount on page xiii, explaining the dramatisation of the circulatory system.

Task: To demonstrate the journey of blood through the human body.

HEAD	HEART
LUNG	LUNG
ARM	ARM
LEG	LEG
BLOOD	BLOOD

OXYGEN   OXYGEN   CARBON DIOXIDE   CARBON DIOXIDE

Breathing

Objective: Develops an understanding of the role of the respiratory system.

Materials

- balloons (one per pupil), timer

▼ Motivate

- Give each pupil a balloon and ask them to count how many breaths it takes to blow the balloon up. Discuss how different people take a different number of breaths to blow up a balloon.

- Ask pupils to take a deep breath while placing their hands flat on their stomach. What do they feel? Why do they think it happens?

▼ Experience

- Distribute and read the worksheet.

- Follow the steps to count breaths before and after exercise. Pupils should note that, after a work-out, the body needs to take in more oxygen, because the blood is pumping around the body faster and the cells need more oxygen.

> **Safety note:** Remind pupils that they should not push themselves to the point of breathlessness.
> Observe pupils with minimal fitness carefully.

- Organise pupils into small groups to discuss what is happening and why they think their breathing increased. Once groups have had time to discuss their theories, share ideas as a class.

- Study the diagram showing the parts of the respiratory system. Ask pupils to locate each part on the outside of their body.

- Pupils complete the activity.

▼ Explain

- Discuss the role of the respiratory system.

> The objective of the respiratory system is to provide oxygen to every cell in the body. We take approximately 20 breaths every minute in order to achieve this. The system follows a process that we don't even have to think about—it happens automatically.
>
> 1. We take in oxygen through our nose. The nose filters, moistens and warms the air.
>
> 2. The air then moves down the trachea to the bronchi, which feed the air into the lungs.
>
> 3. When in the lungs, the alveoli work to transfer the oxygen into the blood.
>
> 4. The blood then transports the oxygen to the various cells in our body, and returns the waste product, carbon dioxide, back to the lungs. It is then exhaled through the mouth.
>
> The diaphragm also helps us to breathe. It is a muscle, and as it pulls down, it provides more space for our lungs to fill and expand. As it pushes up, it forces the air out of our lungs, causing them to contract.

▼ Apply

- Pupils consider how smoking affects the respiratory system.

- Discuss this topic in small groups, recording ideas in note form and then sharing them with the class. Pupils may like to establish a no smoking campaign, utilising the knowledge they have gained about the lungs.

▼ Review and reflect

- Pupils complete a 'Before and after' chart on page xvii about the respiratory system.

▼ Answers

What I've learned

1.

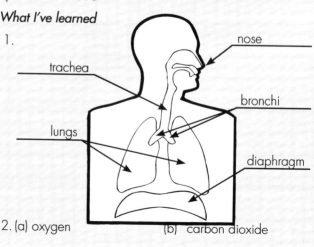

nose

trachea

bronchi

lungs

diaphragm

2. (a) oxygen   (b) carbon dioxide

Breathing

Task: To understand the role of the respiratory system.

▶ What to do:

1. While sitting, time yourself for one minute and count how many breaths you take. _____ breaths

2. Run at a steady pace for five minutes, then stop.

3. Time yourself for one minute and count how many breaths you now take. _____ breaths

4. Discuss what you notice about your breathing and record your observations.

5. Discuss why you think the changes occurred and record your thoughts.

▶ What I've learned

1. Use the labels below to complete the diagram of the respiratory system.

| nose | lungs | bronchi | diaphragm | trachea (windpipe) |

2. Complete these sentences using the words in the box.

    (a) When we inhale, we take in _____.

    (b) When we exhale, we let out _____.

carbon dioxide

oxygen

Your bones

Objective: Cuts out a skeleton and joins it together correctly.

Materials:

• A4 paper, scissors, glue, pencils

▼ Motivate

• Ask pupils to stand in a circle to sing and perform the 'hokey-cokey'.

• Discuss with pupils how our bones help us to stand upright and how our muscles work with our bones and joints to make us move. Ask pupils to hold their upper arm and bend their elbow in an upward motion: What do they feel? Repeat with the leg, hold the thigh and bend the knee: What do they feel?

• Encourage pupils to 'feel' their body; the hardness of their sternum, softness of their tummy. Feel the feet and hands, there are many bones there. Talk about the joints in the fingers that allow them to bend. Where else on your body do they have a joint?

▼ Experience

• Distribute and read the worksheet. Study the skeleton pieces.

• Pupils cut out the body shape and glue it in the middle of a separate sheet of A4 paper.

• Pupils cut out the pieces and glue them in place to make the skeleton.

• Read the labels. Talk about the body parts in relation to pupils' bodies, then ask them to write these labels next to the skeleton.

• Sing the song 'Dem dry bones' with the pupils to reinforce where each bone belongs in the body. (Lyrics available at <www.kididdles.com/lyrics/d009.html>)

▼ Explain

• Discuss the three jobs of the skeletal system with pupils.

There are 206 bones in the body, known collectively as the skeleton. The skeleton has three jobs:

1. To protect our body parts – The skull protects the brain, ribs protect the heart and lungs and the spine protects the spinal cord.

2. To support our body – The skeleton allows us to stand upright and holds up our internal organs.

3. To help us move – Muscles are joined to our bones. Our bones have joints which enable the skeleton to bend. Joints and ligaments connect the bones to each other. Within the joints is cartilage that enables smooth movement.

▼ Apply

• Pupils study pictures of the skeletons of various other animals; e.g. gorilla, elephant, snake, fish. Pupils note how each animal has bones that protect body parts, how the skeleton supports the body and have various joints that help the animal to move. Pupils should identify that all skeletons have the same purpose.

• Record observations noted during this activity.

▼ Review and reflect

• Use straws and modelling clay to 'invent' a skeleton for a new and amazing creature never before seen. Pupils should apply the knowledge they have learnt about the role of the skeleton and the various bones and joints which make movement possible.

• Pupils complete the science report on page xii after they have completed their model.

▼ Answers

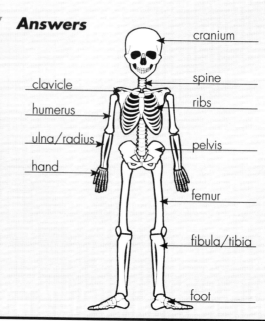

cranium

spine

clavicle

humerus

ribs

ulna/radius

hand

pelvis

femur

fibula/tibia

foot

Your bones

Task: To make a skeleton using the bones on this page.

▶ *What to do:*

1. Cut out the body shape and glue it in the middle of the A4 paper.

2. Cut out the bones.

3. Glue the bones in the correct position on the body shape; starting with the spine, then the ribs and then the pelvis.

4. Find these bones on the skeleton and label them:

cranium	femur	ribs	humerus	spine	fibula/tibia
clavicle	pelvis		hand	foot	ulna/radius

You will need

A4 paper

scissors

glue

pencils

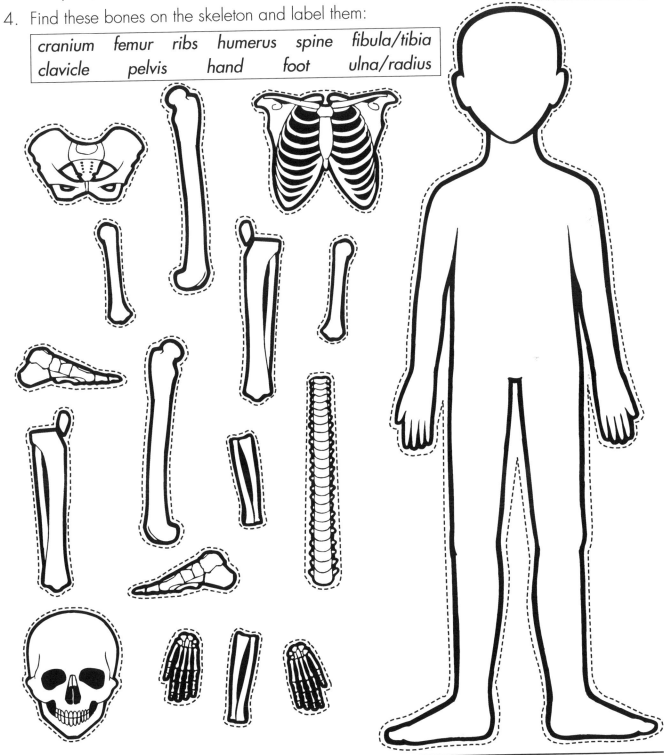

Exercise and heart rate

Objective: Investigates how the heart rate changes with exercise.

Materials

- Motivate – modelling clay, toothpicks
- Experience – stopwatch, exercise equipment such as skipping-rope or ball, an area big enough for the class to complete physical activities

▼ Motivate

- Ask pupils: What is your pulse? Can you feel it? Which fingers should you use to feel your pulse? (pointer and middle finger)

- Ask a pupil to volunteer to show and explain to the class how to find his/her pulse.

- Ask: How can you tell when your heart is beating faster? (breathing faster, can feel heart beating faster)

- Place a toothpick on a small ball of modelling clay and balance it on your wrist where the pulse can be felt. Can pupils see it moving?

▼ Experience

Safety note: Remind pupils that they should not push themselves to the point of breathlessness.
Observe pupils with minimal fitness carefully.

- Practise taking pulse rates by counting the beats for 30 seconds and multiplying the number of beats by two to give a pulse rate in beats per minute (BPM). Pupils may need to take their resting pulse rate a number of times to check for accuracy.

- Record the resting pulse rate on the sheet.

- Follow the steps on the sheet. Pupils may choose an activity that requires equipment, such as a skipping-rope or basketball, but there are many activities that do not require equipment; such as star jumps, running on spot, walking up and down stairs etc.

- Pupils complete the tables until their pulse rate has once again reached the resting rate. Pupils can share with the class how many minutes it took for their pulse to return to its resting rate.

▼ Explain

- Pupils write a sentence summarising their understanding of how exercise effects heart rate.

> The heart is a muscle that acts like a pump pushing blood around the whole body. The muscles in our bodies need the oxygen in the blood to work. When we exercise, the muscles need more oxygen so the heart must beat faster and you breathe faster to get more oxygen to the muscles. The heart beat can be felt as a pulse around the body in the wrist and the neck.
>
> The fitter you are, the slower your heart has to pump the blood around the body and the heart will return to its normal resting rate faster after exercise.

▼ Apply

- Pupils choose five new physical activities of different levels (such as running on spot, dribbling a basketball, stepping up and down stairs, star jumps, walking etc.) and predict their own pulse rate after one minute of each activity. Pupils test his/her predictions by completing the activities and measuring their pulse rates.

▼ Review and reflect

- Pupils teach a group of younger pupils how to take their own pulse. They repeat the above activity with the younger pupils, asking them to do an intense physical activity of their choice for one minute and checking their pulse rate again to see how it has changed. The pupils explain to the younger group why their pulse rate has increased after exercise.

Exercise and heart rate

Task: To investigate how your heart rate changes with exercise.

You will need

a partner

stopwatch

exercise equipment

▶ What to do:

1. Take your resting pulse for 30 seconds.

   [ ] x 2 = [ ] beats per minute (BPM)

2. Choose a physical activity and do it for one minute while your partner times you.

   The activity I chose was: _____

3. Take your pulse again and every minute after, until it returns to your normal resting rate. (Remember to count the beats for 30 seconds then times them by 2.)

Time (minutes)	0	1	2	3	4	5
Pulse rate (BPM)						

4. Choose another physical activity.

   (a) The activity I choose is: _____

   (b) I think my pulse will beat | *faster* | *slower* | than the first activity because:

   _____

▶ What happened?

Do the new activity for one minute while your partner times you, then take your pulse every minute after until it returns to your resting pulse rate.

Time (minutes)	0	1	2	3	4	5
Pulse rate (BPM)						

My prediction was | *correct* | *incorrect* |

▶ What I've learned

Write a sentence explaining how your heart rate changes with exercise.

_____

_____

Chocolate krispies

Objective: Makes a chocolate treat by melting and cooling chocolate (a reversible change).

Materials

- cooking chocolate, rice krispies, hundreds and thousands or mini marshmallows (optional), muffin pan with cases, heat-resistant bowl, saucepan to hold bowl, wooden spoon, kettle, water, oven gloves

▼ Motivate

- Ask: How can these materials be changed to delicious chocolate krispies?
- Ask: What needs to happen to the chocolate before it can blend with the rice krispies?
- Ask: What is required to cause the change?
- Ask: What is required to reverse the change?

▼ Experience

> **Safety note:** Keep pupils well away from boiling water as it is being poured and ensure that adults are supervising pupils as they stir melting chocolate.
>
> Ensure all implements, surfaces and hands are thoroughly cleaned before beginning.

- Pupils follow the procedure, wearing oven gloves to protect themselves from heat of pan and hot water.
- Ask pupils to describe the change to the state of the chocolate as it occurs. (It becomes runny and smooth, perfect for blending with krispies.)
- It is possible to eat the krispies immediately, but it is better to let them cool: Why? (The chocolate cools, becoming more solid and less sticky.)

▼ Explain

- Heating the chocolate caused it to melt and blending could occur. Cooling returned the chocolate to a solid form, holding the krispies in place. This is a reversible change.

> *As a solid is heated, it begins to melt. Heat enters the substance as potential energy and breaks the bonds between the molecules. They are no longer held in a rigid form, so the substance is more fluid.*
>
> *In the change of state from liquid to solid, heat leaves the liquid and the molecular bonding is returned to its rigid state.*

▼ Apply

- Ask pupils to record and explain another reversible change of state; e.g. ice to water to steam.
- Ask: How can a reversible change of state be altered? For example, dissolving something in water.
- Ask: Why do local councils put salt or grit on the roads in icy conditions?

▼ Review and reflect

- On A4 paper folded in half, pupils write a procedure for making chocolate krispies, with the ingredients and method on the left-hand side and comments on the right-hand side. These comments should reflect each pupil's personal understanding and appreciation of the activity, including suggestions for changing or developing the procedure.

▼ Answers

What I've learned

1. (a) melts

   (b) goes hard (solidifies)

   (c) liquids, solids, reversible

Chocolate krispies

Task: To make chocolate krispies by melting and cooling chocolate.

You will need

cooking chocolate

rice krispies

hundreds and thousands or mini marshmallows (optional)

muffin pan with cupcake cases

heat-resistant bowl

saucepan

wooden spoon

kettle

water

oven gloves

▶ What to do:

Safety first! Take care when using hot water.

1. Break chocolate into pieces and place in heat-resistant bowl.

2. Place bowl into saucepan and pour hot water into pan to cover base of bowl.

3. Stir chocolate as it melts.

4. Add rice krispies and stir until covered with chocolate.

5. Add any extras now (such as hundreds and thousands).

6. Spoon krispie mix into cupcake cases and leave for 30 minutes.

▶ What happened?

1. How was it possible to mix the rice krispies with the chocolate?

_____

_____

2. How was it possible to eat the krispies and not get sticky?

_____

_____

▶ What I've learned

1. Fill in the gaps.

    (a) When chocolate is heated, it _____.

    (b) When runny chocolate is cooled, it _____.

    (c) Heating turns solids to _____ and cooling turns them back

    into _____. This is called a _____ change.

Coloured sugar crystals

Objective: Makes sugar crystals from a saturated sugar solution.

Materials

- heat-resistant glass jar, insulating material (oven gloves, tea towels etc.), sugar, tablespoon, teaspoon, water, kettle, measuring jug, coloured pipe-cleaner, string, barbecue skewer, muslin cloth, food colouring

Motivate

- Demonstrate to the whole class that more sugar will dissolve in hot water than in the same volume of cold water.

- Ask: If more sugar can dissolve in hot water, what happens to that extra sugar when the water cools down?

- Ask pupils if they think it is possible to make a sugar crystal larger than a grain of sugar?

Experience

Safety note: Adult supervision will be required to ensure pupils are not at risk of injury when stirring boiling water.

- Pupils follow the procedure, taking care with the boiling water.

- The procedure must be completed as rapidly as possible before the water cools down. Adding insulating material will slow the cooling process.

- The pupils may examine their jars more regularly than every 48 hours, but they may not observe noticeable change.

Explain

- As the class demonstration shows, the solubility of sugar in water increases with an increase in temperature of the water.

- The muslin cloth is used to allow evaporation of water but prevent airborne contamination. Evaporation and cooling will force the sugar molecules to dry in the solution and they will collect on the pipe-cleaner.

- If the water cools down slowly, larger crystals will form.

The solubility of a substance in water refers to the amount that can dissolve in a given volume of water at a given temperature. The substance being dissolved is called the solute and the water is the solvent. The resultant compound is called the solution. Adding solute to the point that no more will dissolve creates a saturated solution.

Heating the water creates more rapid movement and collisions between water and sugar molecules. The energy created by these collisions allows more sugar to be dissolved.

Apply

- Research a recipe for making toffee or fudge and note the instructions for heating and cooling within the process. Make the toffee or fudge, following the instructions correctly as a control and then a second time, deliberately altering the heating and/or cooling instructions. What effect does this have on the end product?

Review and reflect

- Pupils use the knowledge they have gained from the activity to prepare an illustrated explanation of dissolving.

Answers

What I've learned

1. boiling

2. saturated

3. cooled

4. space

5. solution

6. crystals

Coloured sugar crystals

Task: To make sugar crystals from a saturated solution.

You will need

heat-resistant glass jar

insulating material

sugar

tablespoon

teaspoon

water

kettle

measuring jug

coloured pipe-cleaner

string

barbecue skewer

muslin cloth

food colouring

▶ What to do:

1. Wrap glass jar in insulating material.

2. After an adult pours 500 mL boiling water into the glass jar, add some drops of food colouring. *Safety first! Take care when using hot water.*

3. Working quickly, add sugar a tablespoon at a time, stirring constantly with the teaspoon. Continue adding sugar until no more will dissolve.

4. Bend the pipe-cleaner into a shape and attach, with a length of string, to the barbecue skewer.

5. Drop the shape into the jar. It must be fully covered by the solution but not touching the bottom of the jar.

6. Lay the skewer across the jar and cover with the muslin cloth.

7. Place the insulated jar in a safe location away from draughts where it will not be disturbed.

8. After 24 hours, carefully remove the insulating material without disturbing the solution.

▶ What happened?

Every 48 hours, examine the pipe-cleaner for crystal growth and record your observations.

▶ What I've learned

Fill in the gaps using words from the box.

space	saturated	crystals	boiling	solution	cooled

Dissolving the sugar in _____¹ water created a _____²

solution. When the solution _____³, there was not enough

_____⁴ for all the sugar crystals to be dissolved, so they hardened in the

_____⁵ and formed _____⁶ on the pipe-cleaner.

Acid or base

Objective: Makes and uses an indicator to determine the pH of a number of solutions.

Materials

- chopped red cabbage, kettle, water, bowl, sieve, 6 small glass jars, 6 household solutions to test (e.g. lemon juice, white vinegar, baking soda, washing powder, surface cleaner), 5 mL eye-dropper

▼ Motivate

- Ask: What is an acid? What is a base? Do you know of any acids or bases? (car battery acid)

- Ask: What is pH? Do you know why it might be important? (swimming pool testing, soil types)

▼ Experience

Safety note: Adult supervision will be required to ensure that pupils are not at risk of injury from boiling water.

- Pupils follow the procedure for making and testing the pH indicator.

- Depending on local geology, water should be neutral; as should the cabbage indicator. Variations are likely to occur in different areas. The colour changes will depend on how strongly acidic or base a solution is. A strong acid will be red and a weak one purple/red.

- Pupils should not be exposed to strong acids or bases but a demonstration performed by the teacher may help to clarify the pupils' understanding of the concept.

▼ Explain

- As the cabbage indicator is added to each solution, a colour change occurs, dependent on the strength of the acid or base.

All solutions have a degree of acidity or pH value which can be measured. This can be calculated using an indicator or with litmus paper. For greater precision, a pH meter can be used which gives an accurate reading ranging from 1 (very acidic) through to 7 (neutral) and on to 14 (base/alkaline).

Acids and bases can alter the colour of vegetable matter. Red cabbage contains the pigment flavin. This purple pigment turns red in strong acidic solutions and yellow/green in base/alkaline solutions. In such extreme conditions, the ionic structure of the pigment alters to the extent that the molecule absorbs light and, therefore, reflects light at different frequencies, giving the change in colour.

▼ Apply

- Record the use of acids and bases in the home.

- Research how swimming pool water is tested and which chemicals are added to balance the pH.

- Plan an experiment to test the pH of local soils. How might the soil pH affect the choice of plants?

▼ Review and reflect

- Pupils complete a science report (see page xii) describing what they have learned from the activity. Pupils should be encouraged to include how he/she might adapt and improve the procedure.

Acid or base

Task:	To make and test a pH indicator.

You will need

chopped red cabbage

kettle

water

bowl

sieve

six small glass jars

6 samples to test

5 mL eye-dropper

▶ What to do:

Safety first! Take care with the electrical appliance, boiling water and cleaning fluids!

1. Make the pH indicator.
   - (a) Place two handfuls of chopped red cabbage into the bowl.
   - (b) Boil a kettle of water. Add enough water to the bowl to cover the cabbage.
   - (c) Leave to stand until cold.
   - (d) Pour the cabbage and water through the sieve.
   - (e) Keep the liquid and throw away the cabbage in the bin.

2. Test the pH indicator.
   - (a) Label the six jars from 'A' to 'F'.
   - (b) Half-fill the jars, each with a different sample to be tested.
   - (c) In the table below, write the type of the sample next to each letter.
   - (d) Add the red cabbage pH indicator to each jar using the eye-dropper.
   - (e) Note how many drops it takes for the sample to change colour.

▶ What happened?

- Complete the table.

Acid	Neutral	Alkali
red	purple	yellow/green

Sample	Name	Number of drops	Colour change	Acid/Alkali/Neutral
A				
B				
C				
D				
E				
F				

▶ What I've learned

1. What does the number of drops required tell you about the strength of the solution?

_____

2. What you have learned about pH, acids and bases?

_____

Drying day weather

Objective: Constructs a fair test to determine optimum conditions for evaporation.

Materials

- 6 pieces of cloth (white handkerchiefs would be ideal), 12 wooden chopsticks, string, scissors, 12 drawing pins, water, stapler, 6 stopwatches

---

▼ Motivate

- Ask pupils to list what factors they think will affect the drying rate of clothes on a washing line.

- Ask: During which seasons do people dry clothes outdoors on a line?

- Ask: At what time of the year are people more likely to use a tumble drier for drying clothes? Why?

- Ask: How long does a load of washing need to be left on the line, (a) in the summer; (b) in the winter? Why is there a difference?

▼ Experience

- Pupils discuss how to make the test fair, keeping all conditions the same except for the location. If they use white handkerchiefs, not only will the fabric be identical in size and texture but it will be easy to determine the point at which they can be considered dry. Demonstrate this to the pupils beforehand.

- Pupils should choose locations that vary in conditions; such as full sun and windy, full sun and still, part shade and windy, part shade and still, full shade and windy, full shade and still. If there is no wind, fans could be set up to create the effect, but they must be placed at the same setting and distance from the 'washing lines'.

- Pupils need to determine when to start the stopwatches. It must be at the same point in the test for all cloths.

▼ Explain

- The cloth located in the full sun and wind position will dry the quickest. The cloth in the full shade and still location will take the longest to dry.

- On hot days during the summer, the differences in drying times will be less than on cool autumn or spring days. Sunny winter days will give the greatest difference in drying times because the difference in temperature between full sun and full shade is greater and the effect of the wind is greater as the air has a higher moisture content.

Water evaporates at all temperatures, but it occurs more quickly when it is warmer.

Wind speeds up the process of evaporation because the evaporated water is immediately blown away from the cloth, increasing the rate of evaporation. On a still day, the evaporated water remains close to the cloth, reducing the rate of evaporation.

▼ Apply

- Observe the location of washing lines in gardens: Where is the most common location?

- Note how long it takes different materials from the same washing load to dry.

▼ Review and reflect

- Ask: Do you feel this test was a good demonstration of evaporation?

- Pupils complete the science report on page xii, describing the test and how they felt about their prediction and results; including any alterations they might make if they were to repeat it.

Drying day weather

Task: To devise a fair test to determine the best location for a washing line.

You will need

6 pieces of cloth

12 wooden chopsticks

string

scissors

12 drawing-pins

water

stapler

6 stopwatches

▶ What to do:

1. Make six 'washing lines' by using the drawing pins to secure a length of string between two wooden chopsticks.

2. Choose six areas outdoors to erect the 'washing lines'.

3. Wet the pieces of cloth and attach to the lines using staples.

4. Determine how long it takes for each cloth to dry.

5. What steps have you taken to ensure the test is fair?

_____

_____

▶ What will happen?

Which location do you think will be the best for drying?

_____

▶ What happened?

Cloth	Location	Time to dry
A		
B		
C		
D		
E		
F		

▶ What I've learned

The best location for a washing line is

[   ]

because _____

_____

_____

_____

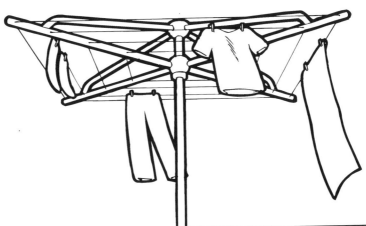

Breakfast included!

Objective: Causes irreversible changes to food by cooking.

Materials

- 2 slices of fresh bread, 1 raw egg, 100 mL cold milk, electric toaster, small bowl, whisk, microwave oven with splatter cover, power supply, 2 plates, 2 knives and forks, salt and pepper to taste

---

▼ Motivate

- Ask pupils: Which foods can be eaten as they are?
- Ask: What are some of the different ways food can be changed before being eaten?
- Ask: How does each method of preparing the food change it?
- Ask: Can any of the changes to the food be reversed?

▼ Experience

Safety note: Teachers must ensure that pupils do not burn themselves when removing the food from the microwave or taking the splatter cover off the bowl.

- Pupils follow the steps of the procedure, describing the physical appearance of the food after each step and how it has altered from its original state.

- There are many variations to the basic scrambled egg recipe and the exact method of cooking. As microwave ovens vary in power and efficiency, the time and setting have not been included on the pupil sheet.

▼ Explain

- The beating process blends the yolk and white of the egg with the milk to form a homogeneous mix. This mix solidifies during the cooking process. The changes which occur at these two stages are chemical changes and cannot be reversed.

- Toasting is a method of controlled burning. The surface of the bread is charred and becomes crisp. Factors affecting the toasting process are: thickness of bread slice, strength of fire source, distance from source and duration of toasting.

Eggs are mostly proteins which are denatured by heat. That is, the internal bonds within the proteins are broken down and the protein changes its molecular structure, turning the liquid egg into a solid. Because the yolk and the white are denatured at different temperatures, we can enjoy 'soft-boiled' eggs where the white is firm but the yolk is still runny.

In toasting, charring causes the formation of carbon on the surface of the bread. This process is called carbonisation.

▼ Apply

- Pupils record irreversible changes witnessed in the kitchen at home over a week. These can be classified in different ways; for example, changes: from liquid to solid (eggs), in size and texture (rice and pasta), from liquid and one solid to another solid (jelly).

▼ Review and reflect

- On A3 paper, pupils create a labelled, diagrammatic representation of the process of making scrambled eggs on toast. They include as much information as they can and use it to describe the irreversible changes involved to another group of pupils.

▼ Answers

What I've learned

1. An irreversible change is a change that cannot be undone.

2. The cooking procedure has caused irreversible changes to the food.

Breakfast included!

Task: To make scrambled egg on toast for two.

What to do:

1. (a) Wash hands thoroughly with warm soapy water.

   (b) Wash and dry all equipment and surfaces thoroughly.

2. Follow the procedure and describe the physical appearance of the food after each stage.

Procedure	Description
Crack **egg** into bowl.	
Add **milk**.	
Whisk **egg and milk** thoroughly.	
Place **fresh bread** in toaster.	
Microwave **egg mix**.	
Remove **toast**.	
Serve and enjoy!	

Safety first! Take care with the electrical appliance and moving hot food.

You will need

2 slices of fresh bread

1 raw egg

100 mL cold milk

electric toaster

small bowl

whisk

microwave oven with splatter cover

power supply

2 plates

2 knives and forks

salt and pepper to taste

What I've learned

1. If a 'reversible change' is one that can return to its original state, what is an 'irreversible change'?

   _____

   _____

2. Rearrange the words of this sentence so it makes sense:

   caused The has changes to irreversible the procedure food. cooking

   _____

Keeping your cool

Objective: Determines the most efficient insulating material from a variety of options.

Materials

- 10 rectangles and 10 squares of the same material, needle and thread, samples of five 'insulating materials' (e.g. polystyrene beads, shredded newspaper, kapok, feathers, pasta shells, wool, plastic pieces cut from yogurt pots), six plastic cups, 15 elastic bands, ice cubes, 6 thermometers

▼ Motivate

- Ask: Why do we need insulating materials?

- Ask: What do you know of that requires insulating? Insulating from what? (heat, cold, sound)

- Look at the samples of insulating materials; discuss their physical appearance and possible insulating efficiency.

▼ Experience

- Pupils follow the procedure, recording their results for each sample.

- Discuss fair testing; for example: deciding how much material to place in each 'jacket and hat', how many people should read the thermometers, and where to place the plastic cups.

▼ Explain

- Some materials are better insulators than others, so the time taken for each to reach a steady temperature will vary. The sample that takes the longest to warm up and maintain that temperature is the most efficient insulator of the samples tested.

> *Heat energy flows from a warmer medium to a cooler one. Insulation works by slowing down the rate of this heat transference. The amount of insulation required depends on the insulating product and the conditions under which it is required to work.*

▼ Apply

- Ask: How could this activity be adapted to test the insulating efficiency of materials against cold and sound?

- Research to make a list of the most popular insulating materials used in the home, from house construction materials to kitchen requirements.

▼ Review and reflect

- Pupils write a science report (page xii) about the activity and construct a graph to show their results.

- Pupils discuss how the ambient temperature of the room may affect the rate of temperature change.

Keeping your cool

Task: To test a selection of materials for their insulating properties.

You will need

10 rectangles (about 30 cm x 10 cm) and 10 squares (about 10 cm x 10 cm) of material

needle and thread

samples of 5 'insulating materials'

6 plastic cups

15 elastic bands

ice cubes

6 thermometers

What to do:

1. Using simple running stitch, sew two rectangles together along three sides to make a large pocket and two squares to make a smaller pocket.

2. Add enough of one type of insulating material to both pockets to make an insulating 'jacket' (rectangle) and 'hat' (square) for a plastic cup. Complete the stitching on the fourth side.

3. Repeat to make four more of each type of insulator, using a different insulating material each time.

4. Use rubber bands to secure the 'jackets' around each cup, leaving one without insulation.

5. Label the cups 'A' to 'F'.

6. Fill each cup to the same level with ice, place a thermometer in each and quickly secure the 'hat' on top of each one.

What happened?

1. Record the temperature in each cup after 30 minutes, 1 hour, 2 hours and 4 hours.

2. Which materials kept the ice-water mix cooler for longer? 1 for best insulator, 6 for worst.

Sample	A	B	C	D	E	F
Temperature (30 min)						
Temperature (1 hour)						
Temperature (2 hours)						
Temperature (4 hours)						
Results						

What I've learned

Explain the results of your test.

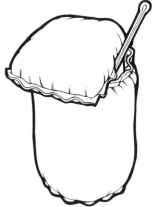

Wonder cloth

Objective: Conducts a fair test to compare absorbency of a range of materials.

Materials

- 6 different materials (newspaper, paper, fabric, toilet paper etc.), measuring jug, measuring cylinder, plastic funnel, stopwatch, shallow bowl, water, scissors

▼ Motivate

- Look at the similarities and differences between the materials: softness, weave, stretch, texture.

- Discuss possible uses for each material.

- Ask: Why is absorbency an important property to consider when choosing a material for a kitchen cloth and a raincoat?

- Ask: Why is it important to choose the best material for the job? (Include materials such as glass, wood and plastics in this discussion.)

- Ask: What external factors might affect absorbency?

▼ Experience

- Pupils follow the procedure to test the materials for absorbency. Discuss the concept and importance of a 'fair test'.

- How can pupils set up their tests to ensure 'maximum fairness'? (exactly when to start stopwatch, ensuring no drips from the material before measuring)

▼ Explain

- The most absorbent material is the one which collects the maximum amount of water in the given time.

> Absorption is a process in which one substance is drawn in by another substance (usually porous). In the case of this activity, the water is collected by the sample material. There are other types of absorption, such as light, heat and sound.
>
> The absorption properties of materials are important in determining which material is the best one for a given purpose.

▼ Apply

- Pupils describe a fair test to determine the water absorbency of a number of grades of paper: Which of their samples would be the best for use as a disposable kitchen towel?

- Pupils record examples of materials in the home used for their absorbency properties; e.g. heat, light and sound.

▼ Review and reflect

- Pupils conduct the same test with a group of younger pupils; explaining each step of the procedure and the importance of fair testing.

Wonder cloth

Task: To test a number of materials to find the one with greatest absorbency.

You will need

6 different materials

measuring jug

measuring cylinder

plastic funnel

stopwatch

shallow bowl

water

scissors

▷ **What to do:**

1. Measure and cut pieces of each material, ensuring they are of equal size.

2. Label the materials from 'A' to 'F'.

3. Add a litre of water to the bowl.

4. Place the first piece of material in the bowl and start the stopwatch.

5. After 10 seconds, remove the material from the bowl.

6. Squeeze out the absorbed water into the measuring cylinder, using the funnel.

7. Record the amount of water collected in the measuring cylinder on the table below.

8. Repeat for all material samples and add the information to the table.

▷ **What happened?**

Material	A	B	C	D	E	F
Volume of water collected (mL)						

▷ **What I've learned**

1. Use your results to rank the sample materials from greatest to least absorbency.

_____   _____

_____   _____

_____   _____

2. I think the test was fair/unfair because

_____

_____

_____

_____

_____

How much air?

Objective: Determines relationship between size of particle and volume of air trapped between.

Materials

- samples of 6 grades of cleaned stones (chippings and pea gravel from garden stores are ideal), 6 identical jars (jam jars), measuring cylinder, scoop, water, plastic funnel

▼ Motivate

- Look at the samples and discuss their physical appearance.
- Ask pupils: What is between the stones? (nothing?)
- Ask: How can the volume of air be measured?

▼ Experience

- Pupils follow the procedure and should discover that the biggest stones require the greatest volume of water to overflow the jar.
- Pupils must ensure that the test is fair. The jars must be the same size and filled to the brim. Water must be added until it overflows.
- When recording the volume of water, pupils must read the scale on the measuring cylinder from the bottom of the meniscus of the surface of the water.

▼ Explain

- The water collected from the smallest stones was less than that collected from the largest stones. A graphical representation would show that, as the size of the stones increase, so does the volume of water required to overflow the jar. As the water replaces the air trapped between the stones, this means there is less air trapped between smaller stones than between larger stones.

> Small stones fit more closely together, leaving smaller gaps between, so the volume of trapped air is small. Larger stones do not fit so well together, leaving bigger gaps between, therefore trapping more air.

▼ Apply

- How could this activity be adapted to test the density of different soils? For example; light sand soils which air can flow through to heavy clay soils which clump together.

▼ Review and reflect

- Pupils explain the steps taken to ensure the test was fair and suggest how the accuracy of the results can be tested; for example: by repeating readings, more than one person recording the same results.

How much air?

Task: To find the volume of air trapped between stones of different sizes.

You will need

samples of 6 different-sized stones

6 identical jars

measuring cylinder

scoop

water

plastic funnel

▶ **What to do:**

1. Fill each jar with one of the six samples until the stones are level with the top of the jar.

2. Label jars from 'A' (the smaller stones) to 'F' (the largest stones).

3. Add water to each jar until it overflows.

4. Use the funnel to transfer the water from each jar into the measuring cylinder.

5. Record the volume of water from each sample jar on the table below.

▶ **What happened?**

1. What did you notice as water was added to each jar?

_____

2. Draw a sketch of each stone sample.

Sample	A	B	C	D	E	F
Sketch						
Volume collected (mL)						

▶ **What I've learned**

1. Explain what happened as water was added to each jar.

_____

_____

2. Explain why stones of different sizes gave different water volume readings.

_____

_____

Salt, pepper and bean mix-up

Objectives: •   Separates a mixture of different solids.

•   Explains how the method of separation works.

Materials

•   sea salt crystals, black peppercorns and mill, dried beans (larger than colander holes), teaspoon (for salt and peppercorns), tablespoon (for beans), tweezers, kitchen sieve, small colander, large bowl for mixing.

▼ Motivate

•   Ask pupils to describe the appearance of the salt crystals, peppercorns and dried beans and note similarities and differences.

•   Ask: What happens to pepper in the mill?

•   Ask: How might tweezers be used for separating materials?

•   Ask: What is the difference between the sieve and the colander?

▼ Experience

•   Ask pupils to mix a spoonful of each material in the bowl. Using each implement in turn, pupils try to separate all three materials. They record their observations by completing Question 3 in 'What to do – 1'.

•   Pupils grind a spoonful of peppercorns and should discuss how its appearance has altered. They mix the pepper grinds with a spoonful each of salt crystals and dried beans.

•   By discussing the properties of each implement and the size and appearance of each material, pupils consider how all three implements may be used to separate the three materials. They record their observations by completing Question 4 in 'What to do – 2'.

▼ Explain

•   Pupils complete the 'What I have learned' section to explain what happened and show what they have learnt.

Solid materials can be separated from one another when either;

•   the particles are large enough and different in appearance so they may be separated manually.

•   the particles of each material are of different size and can be separated by sieving because the large particles cannot pass through holes of a smaller diameter.

A mixture of solid materials of different sizes can be separated in a sieve tower; a series of sieves with holes of decreasing size with a solid base tray beneath the lowest sieve. The sieves are arranged from largest hole size at the top to smallest hole size at the bottom. The mixture is fed into the top sieve and the tower shaken. All particles smaller than the size of the holes of the top sieve, will pass through to the next. This continues until only the particles smaller than the holes in the lowest sieve fall in to the bottom tray.

▼ Apply

•   Pupils complete a labelled scientific diagram from page xvi showing how five different grades of gravel (from coarse to fine) could be separated using a sieve tower. Pupils must clearly show the order of hole size of the sieves and the grade of gravel captured by each sieve.

▼ Review and reflect

•   Pupils role-play a builder explaining to an apprentice how a sieve tower works and how to use it.

▼ Answers

What to do – 2

4. (a) beans, salt crystals, ground pepper

(b) ground pepper, salt crystals, beans

What I've learned

1 - pieces   2 - different

3 - separated   4 - materials

5 - sieving   6 - larger

7 - smaller

Salt, pepper and bean mix-up

Task: To separate mixtures of solid materials using different implements.

You will need

sea salt crystals

black peppercorns and mill

dried beans

teaspoon (for salt and peppercorns)

tablespoon (for beans)

tweezers

kitchen sieve

small colander

bowl for mixing

▶ What to do – 1

1. Mix a teaspoon each of the salt crystals, and peppercorns and a tablespoon of beans in a bowl.

2. Using the tweezers, sieve and colander in turn, try to separate the three materials.

3. Draw lines to match the implement with the explanation of what was separated.

    colander •   • *All the materials were separated.*

    sieve •   • *The beans were separated.*

    tweezers •   • *All the materials stayed mixed up.*

▶ What to do – 2

1. Grind a teaspoon of peppercorns in the mill.

2. Mix the ground pepper with a teaspoon of salt and a tablespoon of beans.

3. Use the tweezers, sieve and colander to separate the three materials.

4. Complete the sentences.

    (a) The tweezers separated all three materials because the _____ and

        _____ could be picked up, leaving the

        _____ in the bowl.

    (b) The sieve could only separate the _____ because the

        _____ and _____ couldn't pass through it.

▶ What I've learned

Choose words to fill the gaps in the sentences.

smaller	different	sieving	materials	separated	larger	pieces

If the _____[1] of each material look _____[2]

and are big enough, they can be _____[3] using tweezers.

Solid _____[4] can also be separated by _____[5]

because _____[6] pieces cannot pass through the

_____[7] holes.